Ryan C. Bolen Jr.

GEMS

(*Frontispiece:*) Jewel-studded crown. Detail from
Jan van Eyck's painting "Adoration of the Lamb."

GEMS

Mab Wilson

A Studio Book

THE VIKING PRESS

New York

To Alexandra and Vicky and Brooke

25 color photographs specially taken for this book by
DAVID PLOWDEN

First published in 1967 by The Viking Press, Inc.
625 Madison Avenue, New York, N.Y. 10022

Published simultaneously in Canada by
The Macmillan Company of Canada Limited

Library of Congress catalog card number: 67-19501
Printed and bound in Italy by Mondadori-Verona

Contents

An Aphrodite of the Hellenistic period, wearing pearl earrings.

Amulet or Adornment?

I

*W*hen man first picked up a flat stone or shell and pasted it to his body with mud or slime, just what did he have in mind?

Did he hope to protect himself from the malignancies of his day, from animals better armed (and toothed) than he? Did he think the shell made some kind of connection between him and whatever (or whoever) made the river fat with fish?

Or, when he plastered that shell to his great hairy chest, was he pinning a pearl in his ascot? As he looked down, chin on chest, did he think it beautiful, or did he think *he* was now beautiful?

Which came first in man's relationship with stones—amulet or adornment? No one knows, and the question remains wide open.

Those who believe that once upon a time man was more godlike and that the best and finer wisdom has been lost, not found, may choose the idea of an amulet: a special stone that related him in some magical three-way parlay to both nature and some higher power. Without question, the earliest form of jewelry was the amulet.

On the other hand, for those who accept the receding brow and length of arm and short thumb of their ancestors there is a fascinating conclusion in Chapter II of Wolfgang Kohler's *The Mentality of Apes* (second revised edition 1926), which presents the view that with those primates, at any rate, the handling of "pretty things" (chains, leaves, bits of twig, rags) was for the purpose of adornment.

> They are fond of carrying quite widely different objects about on the body in one way or another. Almost daily the animals can be seen walking with a rope, a bit of rag, a blade of grass or a twig on their shoulders. If Tsgogo was given a metal chain, she would immediately put it around her neck. Bushes and brambles are carried about in considerable quantities spread over the whole back.
>
> In addition, pieces of rag and string are to be seen hanging in long strings over their shoulders to the ground on both sides of the face. If these things keep on falling down they hold them in their teeth or squeezed under the chin, but, whichever way it is, they must have them dangling. . . . No observer can escape the impression . . . *The objects hanging about the body serve the function of adornment in the widest sense.* [The italics are mine.]

In a less simple way the amulet-adornment question is still open and divides the world into two valid groups: those who love stones and those who love jewelry.

It's been a long, proven-and-documented relationship, and, be it amulet or adornment, at the very core lies the basic question: What is this "thing" man has about stones? The cynic replies, thumbing his fingers, "Value." But stones were treasured before man gave them value. The romantic answers, "Beauty," but that is far too subjective and depends on the eye of the beholder.

Whatever the attraction is, it is strange and strong and one that those who love stones feel and those who love only jewelry miss.

Have you ever looked at an emerald, turning it slowly in the light melted by the gentleness of its glow, only to have it suddenly glare at you, a wild green thing? Have you ever, for a moment, lost track of yourself, led on by the good-and-evil play of a black opal, or instinctively cupped your hand to contain the sky-deep immensity of a pure blue Persian turquoise?

People who react strongly and quickly to stones have certain characteristics. They rarely separate the precious from the semiprecious. They are vague about value, fashion, and "jewelry." They seem to feel that a stone has some kind of meaning or power. They are not especially acquisitive, are quite happy window-shopping, and are apt to personify: to apologize to a kicked table leg or attribute hurt feelings to a neglected stone.

If you are attracted by stones, take heed, as the attraction quickly becomes fascination, and the deeper the fascination the more you see, and the more you see, both literally and figuratively, the more a stone will draw you in and backward, always backward—through history and beyond—until you are standing with the Java man on your right, the tip of a glacier on your left, and aeons of manless history before you.

Space travel and extrasensory perception may draw the imagination forward, but stones, by their very nature, have a way of drawing one to the past. Back through the thousand-watt blaze of the Star of Africa to the glisten of Old Mine diamonds silver-set in a Georgian brooch. Back to the great convoluted balas ruby of Anne de Bretagne, to the cabalist's hyacinth engraved with the magical formula Abracadabra, back to the uncut rubies of Saint Wenceslaus's crown, to a Roman jasper signet ring, a Greek carnelian intaglio, a long Egyptian emerald pierced lengthwise and strung like a bugle bead. Back further to a pale amethyst Chaldean seal, to an eye agate from northern Mesopotamia, back to the smooth-stone age and a handful of shattered quartz in a prehistoric grave.

It is a curious thing that, while men have coveted, stolen, worshiped, and even sold themselves for stones, most of us know practically nothing about them. If we knew as little about other things we value as highly one might tremble for the evolution as well as the economy of the universe.

A few bits of stone lore have, of course, trickled into our fund of general information. Diamonds are so hard one can write on glass with them, and they should be blue-white. Emeralds have flaws. The best kind of ruby is the pigeon-blood, the best sapphire is the Kashmir. Topazes are yellow, zircons are blue, and opals are unlucky. Turquoise comes from the Navajo, the moonstone comes from Wilkie Collins, and Cleopatra drank her pearls—fact and fancy well mixed.

It is a puzzling ignorance, for the deeper one looks into the world of the precious crystal the deeper one's sense of astonishment and delight, for the nether world is a great cosmos in itself—not just the "cellar" of the earth. A closer look at this part-time kingdom of Persephone and the flowers of her dark garden opens up a world quite as awe-inspiring as the ocean floor or the sky. If the sky gives a sense of space and the sea a sense of source, then the nether world gives a sense of time and order, and perhaps a different understanding of the ancient "jingle" of Hermes Trismegistus:

> Happy thou who the riddle readest.
> Stars above, stars below;
> All that is over, under shall show.
> Happy thou who the riddle readest.

When you touch your ring or your pin, you touch the inhabitants of a world that pre-dates us and will outlast us, to such an extent that on the time scale of a stone the whole long history of organic life lies on the surface of the nether world as light and recent as yesterday's dust in the parlor.

Precious stones are the natural citizens of this ancient world. They were fed by the rock jungle, drank from lakes of molten magma, and watched their world crush and eat and overflow cataclysmically onto "our" world. It is hard to understand how such black violence could produce the merry topaz, or the child-eyed aquamarine.

Dumb, somnambulent, and immortal, the precious stones lie there in that realm of black lakes, cathedral-sized caverns, of subcrust mountain ranges, rumbling magma, and tumbling underground rivers. There in that dark country that begins a scant twelve inches under our feet soar architectural shafts of beryl and quartz, pipes of diamonds, proud corundum crystals; there rest the solidified amorphous ones—opal, jet, rock salt —patient and ancient, awaiting two things: light and discipline. For, without light and without cutting and polishing, they are mere pebbles or anonymous streaks in rock— dull, colorless, lifeless. Bringing them to life and light and beauty may be one of the few "good" things that man has done for the earth.

While their antiquity and hardness make them seem motionless and frozen in time, of course they aren't. A kind of evolution and devolution goes on there too. Right this minute a new crystal of tourmaline or amethyst is being formed from the molten magma of the earth's core or from volcanic gases and solutions, and an opal is dying of thirst or metamorphizing into chalcedony. But the whole existence of mankind could come and go while a new crystal forms.

II

Curious Lore

*P*recious stones have had their own historians. The early ones were usually naturalists who often added the local gossip and old tales to their writing. Among the best was Theophrastus, who lived in Greece around 400 B.C. He was a mineralogist as well as a naturalist and, as he was both disciple and literary heir to Aristotle, one must assume a philosopher as well. His identification was so clear and so descriptive that, even though some of the names were hard to untangle, his minerals and crystals are clearly recognizable. It was he who settled the argument as to whether the stone was amber or yellow zircon in the High Priest's Breastplate—on the very sound basis of temperature. The stone was known to be cold, and zircon is a cold crystal, while amber is not.

Perhaps even greater reverence should go to Pliny the Elder, who was born hundreds of years later in 23 A.D. He was a fine and fluent naturalist and mineralogist and, to make him as human as he was wise, an astringent critic of his times. He took pride in acknowledging his "teachers," among whom, of course, was Theophrastus. It was Pliny who first placed the emerald in the proper category, though it took eighteen hundred years to prove him right. His thirst for precise information resulted in his remarkable *Histories*, and also, as it happened, in his death, for in the fateful year of 79 A.D. he was overcome at Pompeii while investigating Vesuvius at too close quarters.

Many lapidaries (a lapidary was like a bestiary) were written during the ensuing years, but, while they added greatly to the information on stones as amulets and stones as medicine, they added very little to the scientific knowledge of stones.

In the early seventeenth century came Anselmus de Boot, who was a mineralogist as well as physician to the Holy Roman Emperor Rudolf II—and those two interests were not so far apart in those days, for stones were still being used therapeutically. Poor Rudolf, with his fits of depression and madness, was in sore need of every carat's worth he got. De Boot's book, written in 1609, is of perhaps greater interest to historians than mineralogists, as he gave the cures-by-stones which were still in current use; also the "true meanings" of stones, as well as their temperature and sex. De Boot's inner struggle comes through clearly in his writings: to stay well away from heresies, to try and rationalize good and evil, to give the stones their due as curative powers, and still not to allow man to fall into "stone worship" and superstition.[1]

People in the fifteenth and sixteenth centuries were deeply concerned with the true properties of stones: metaphysicians and mineralogists continued to struggle for the truth and searched in each other's fields for it.

From the twelfth century the alchemists also had a good deal to say about stones. They made use of them in their experiments and regarded them esoterically as symbols. They had inherited the scientific and therapeutic knowledge of Theophrastus, Aristotle, Pliny, and Hippocrates, but by that time they had also acquired from the East a good deal of knowledge of quite a different sort: chemistry.. Alchemy was the elder science, but alchemy and chemistry cannot be separated; they both deal with the power to transform matter, but alchemy dealt also with man's inner chemistry, the chemistry of his potentials, his inner evolution, his soul, spiritual development, and so on. Alchemy was considered heretical, as it attempted to bypass orthodoxy, and so in an effort to hide the true content a great deal of double talk resulted. "Producing gold from base metal" could be taken either literally or symbolically. There was so much talk about this act, and the efforts continued for so many years—and as no gold resulted—that something other than greed must have been keeping the idea alive. The Philosopher's Stone was what? A diamond? A bit of quartz engraved with the Tetragrammaton? An idea? Like the Grail, no one ever saw it—but the idea was readily accepted. The alchemists did little pounding and powdering of stones and didn't use large ones, but they did drop them into potions, and history doesn't record how they came out: larger, or as a liquid, or as they were, after the "guests" had left.

Between the symbolism of the alchemists, the claims of the charlatans (who outnumbered them considerably), Doctor Dee's "Shewing Stone," John Aubrey's casual encounters with vision-giving crystals, and various handed-down "cures," the public was somewhat bewildered. But happily, above the gabble of confusion, a cool voice is always to be heard. Pliny was clearly exasperated by the mumbo jumbo of "magical stones," and Eusebius, the fourth-century theologian, said angrily that stones "possessed

1. "The supernatural and acting cause is God, the good angel and the evil one; the good by the will of God, and the evil by His permission. . . . What God can do by Himself, He could do also by means of ministers, good and bad angels, who, by special grace of God and for the preservation of men, are enabled to enter precious stones and to guard men from dangers or procure some special grace for them. However, as we may not affirm anything positive touching the presence of angels in gems, to repose trust in them, or to ascribe undue powers to them, is more especially pleasing to the spirit of evil, who transforms himself into an angel of light, steals into the substance of the little gem, and works such wonders by it that some people do not place their trust in God but in a gem, and seek to obtain from it what they should ask of God alone. Thus it is perhaps the spirit of evil which exercises its power on us through the turquoise, teaching us, little by little, that safety is not to be sought from God but from a gem." (*The Curious Lore of Precious Stones.* George F. Kunz [Philadelphia: J. P. Lippincott Company, 1913], p. 5.)

11

no other qualities than natural ones." Then once more, at the beginning of the sixteenth century, Francis Bacon tried to sort things out.

> There are many things that operate on the spirits of man by secret sympathy and antipathy. That precious stones have virtues in the wearing has been anciently and generally received and they are said to produce several effects. So much is true, gems have fine spirits as appears by their splendor and therefore may operate by consent on the spirits of man to strengthen them and exhilarate them. The best stones for this purpose are the diamond, emerald, hyacinth, and yellow topaz.
>
> As for their particular properties no credit can be given them, but it is manifest that light above all things rejoices the spirit of man; and probably varied light has the same effect with greater novelty which may be one cause why stones exhilarate.

The seventeenth century produced a man to whom the world owes a great deal for the knowledge of certain specific stones. He was a delightful Frenchman called Jean Baptiste Tavernier (later Baron Tavernier), and many a famous stone owes its accurate genealogy to his meticulous diaries and records—and purchases. He was a great traveler and trader and knew certain parts of India intimately. He was also an amusing diarist. His interview with Almager, World Shaker (son of Shah Jehan of Taj Mahal fame), is a droll recital. His restless French temperament was checked by the slow, ritualistic build-up of the Mogul's way of presenting a stone. Hours went by while Tavernier listened impatiently to the long history and genealogy of each jewel and waited for silk wrappings to be raised from one great stone after another.

One reason Tavernier was able to have the interview with "World Shaker" was that he was entirely honest in all his dealings with the Indian merchants and had gained their trust. As word of his unusually high ethics traveled to the hierarchy of kings and emirs and maharajas, they too came to respect him. He was one of the few men in all history who was shown the treasures of the various "crowns," for these treasures were not the adornments of the rulers but the wealth of the country. Rulers did not reveal their national resources readily, but they came to realize that he was discreet, that he knew stones thoroughly, and that the appraisals he gave were just and valid, and— very important to those men—they felt that he had the proper feeling about stones. Probably these sixteenth- and seventeenth-century Moguls were no more superstitious than their European brethren, but perhaps they were more open about it. Tavernier himself apparently did not hold with those beliefs and had a very down-to-earth view about stones. Respect, admiration, value, and salability, formed the basis of his relationship to stones, but he was either tolerant enough or tactful enough to hold his peace and nod agreeably when the "tales and meanings" were recited, and so managed to give no offense in a sensitive area. It was Tavernier who provided Louis XIV with a number of great stones, among them the Tavernier Blue, of which the Hope Diamond is a portion.

12

Jean Baptiste Tavernier, diamond merchant. The fur-lined cape and turban were presents from the Shah of Persia.

Later came many Plinys, but fewer lapidaries and De Boots. The age of science was on: mineralogy rather than meanings, physics but not metaphysics, please, was the order, though some few—Dr. George F. Kunz and Mr. Edward Streeter in particular— did keep alive, by recording them, the old superstitions and romances. Now "stone" books have become textbooks, and, while they occasionally contain a tale or history, they are primarily to be read by students of mineralogy and by jewelers or collectors. These books are not as uninteresting as that might sound; they are merely difficult to read. No matter with what clarity and simplicity Messrs. Robert Shipley, Robert Webster, Edward Kraus, Chester Baker Slawson, or G. F. Herbert Smith write, the fact remains that light dispersion, refractive indices, and space lattices are not breakfast reading for most of us.

13

Stone Symbols

III

$\mathcal{T}$he Chaldeans had what one can only call an "instant relationship" with stones. The Chaldeans were primarily astrologers, and they worshiped the luminous moving bodies which—or who—they believed controlled the destinies of men and nations. Over the thousand years that they watched, recorded, and made their astrological calculations, they collected, inadvertently, an enormous fund of pure astronomical information, for which science owes them a great debt.

As soon as they identified a few planets in the heavens they ascribed stones to them, for in their eyes and to their knowledge there was a definite relationship.

It is not certain whether the Babylonians actually "discovered" the zodiac, but the twelve signs appeared in their time. The symbols they used were different—and terrifying, such as the Ravening Dog, the Viper, the Hurricane, and Tiamat, a female who was the origin of all evil. Each had its stone.

The Greeks took the zodiac from the Babylonians, and the Egyptians took it from the Greeks. Then the Persians took it from the Egyptians and passed it on to India, and Indian Buddhist monks took it to China. And wherever it went, and whatever the signs were called, stones were ascribed to them.

From these planetary stones came today's birthstones. At one time these stones were less "individual" and were related rather objectively to that period when a certain planet was in the ascendancy and man's doings at that period were under the planet's influence. An ancient Roman, for instance, with enough superstitions and sesterces, might wear a ring in which were set all twelve stones, or he might have twelve separate rings and wear each in its proper season.

It wasn't until the sixteenth century that—some say in Poland and some say in Germany—the individual birthstones were established, and a man began to think that his own personal birth sign was the only sign of real importance to *him*. It was one step away from collectivism, as were individual coats of arms and the use of last names.

People being what they are—disputatious—and stones being what they were—local—societies didn't always agree as to which was the rightful stone for a certain sign. The list compiled by Dr. G. F. Kunz in his book *The Curious Lore of Precious Stones*

Monoceros, a constellation in the Milky Way

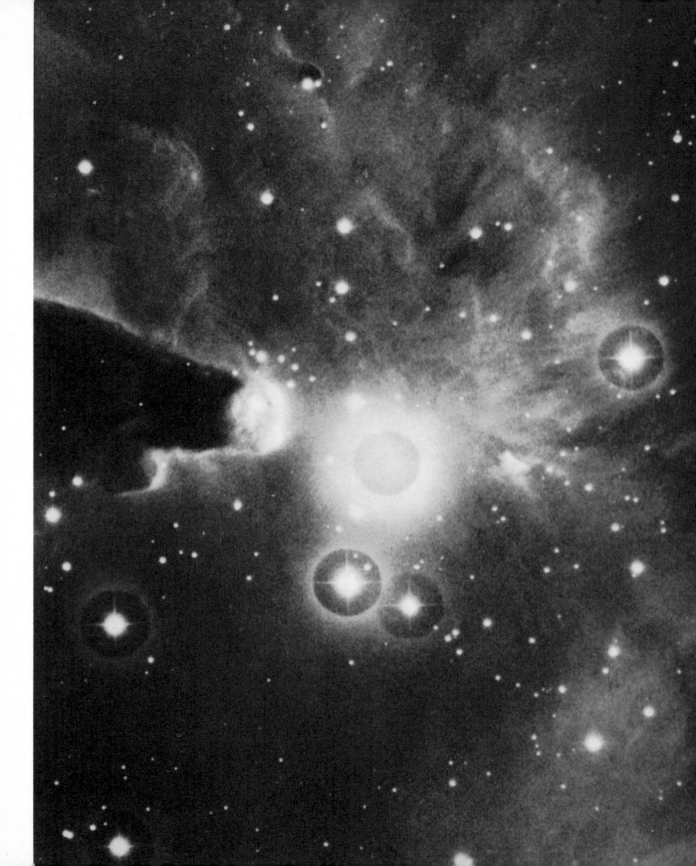

The High Priest's Breastplate, showing the twelve symbolic stones.

(*Opposite:*) Signs of the Zodiac, believed to influence different areas of the body.

shows that certain stones—topaz, garnet, sapphire, amethyst, and beryl—stayed rather firmly fixed in their signs.

Yet, as time wore on and travel increased, there was enough disagreement to unsettle the jewelers who, one imagines, were constantly under attack by astrologically minded ladies for offering them the wrong birthstone or for misrepresenting a planet. Things came to such a pass that in 1913 a great gathering of jewelers met in Kansas City to try to tidy up the seven-thousand-year-old problem, which everyone agreed, while laughing heartily and crossing his fingers behind his back, was all nonsense anyway.

From the solemn bull-throated pronouncements of the Chaldean priests to a group of hot, contentious, irascible jewelers in August in Kansas City was a long time and a far cry, but they finally settled this matter once and for all—by adding alternatives.

Another very clear example of the ascribing of stones is shown in the Breastplate of the High Priest, circa 1300 or 1400 B.C. Whether it was an entirely new inspiration on the part of the Jews, or whether it was the old planetary stones turning up again, can't be said. But the Jews, being monotheists, could not very well worship planets, so possibly the old zodiac signs were taken over and reascribed to the Twelve Tribes of Israel. Whichever it was, there were the stones. When the Christians came along they simply lifted the zodiac-cum-tribe stones and allotted them to the Apostles and also established them as the Foundation Stones of the New Jerusalem. These twelve stones of the High Priest's Breastplate turned up again and again in early royal regalias, making very clear the fact that they had originally some symbolical meaning. Around 4000 B.C. the High Priest of Memphis had a breastplate too, adorned with what appears from the carving to be twelve balls and crosses, but it is impossible to tell if they were of gold or stones.

IV

Art and Nature:
Cut, Flaws, Heat, and Habit

Cut alone unlocks the secret stone, freeing fire, brilliance, and very often color. Cut alone lets a crystal's beauty fly to the light.

Cut had perhaps the slowest evolution of any of the crafts. For thousands of years a polish was the only embellishment, and frequently man had nothing to do with this. He simply chose stones which had already been polished by water and friction against other stones in river beds. Even when goldwork had become exquisitely delicate and sophisticated, the stones used in these finely wrought settings were usually crudely polished and the quality of the stones a very secondary requisite to size or shape.

The softer stone took the highest polish then, and the more obdurate stones could only be buffed a bit so that they shone in areas. It was not until the relative hardness of the various crystals was recognized that the lapidary began the long journey from the rough, polished pebble to the fire and brilliance and augmented color we see today.

The cabochon was the first cut, and in reality it was no cut at all but a smoothing off of rough spots, pits, and uneven corners. Many of the great Indian colored stones still hold their original shape and have never been what one would today call "cut." The harder stone was merely polished along its own planes; a shined-up version of its own natural crystal shape and the first so-called diamond point cut was no more than a diamond's natural octahedron buffed up. Emerald beryls were polished and drilled lengthwise, but little effort was made by the ancients to change their natural shape. Later, when it was discovered that the dust of a harder stone could polish a softer stone (or, as in the case of the diamond, that it could be polished with its own dust), the stones began to be given shapes dictated by man rather than by nature. Sometimes the top of a well-shaped diamond—and sometimes the bottom as well—was polished down to a flat surface, and that was the ancestor of the table-cut stone. A little later, in India, it was discovered that surface flaws of diamonds could be scooped out with diamond dust, oil, and a leather wheel, and that was the first facet. Soon after that the Indians found that by cutting streaky or unevenly pigmented colored stones in a certain way a small patch of color could be made to *appear* to suffuse the entire stone. To this day many a glorious colored stone, looked at along certain angles, will reveal very little color, and in areas none at all.

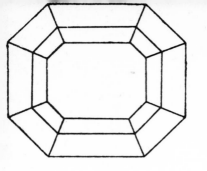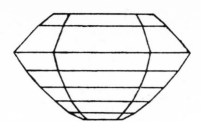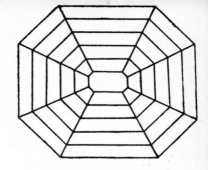

STEP CUT: Top. Side. Lower part.

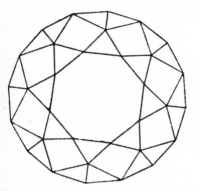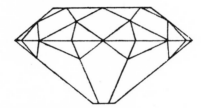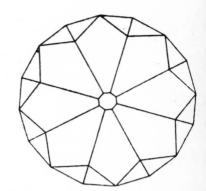

BRILLIANT CUT: Top. Side. Lower part.

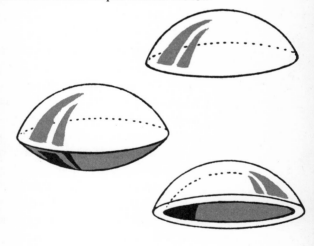

CABOCHON CUTS: Simple. Double. Hollow.

A brilliant-cut diamond.

Individual cuts can have many names, but all cuts fall basically into the three main categories of cabochon, brilliant cut, and step cut. The mark of the brilliant cut is that somewhere it will have triangular facets. The mark of the step cut is parallel facets on the pavilion and usually on the crown. Above are the cuts developed over the centuries.

19

*F*eathers, clouds, spots, streaks, silk, fractures, and inclusions of any kind detract, of course, from the value of any transparent crystal, as they interfere with the light, transparency, and color. At the same time, under a microscope, flaws themselves can be quite as fascinating as the stones they mar. It is not on record that anyone has ever made a collection of flaws (except perhaps Dr. E. J. Gübelin, who wrote a book entitled *Inclusions as a Means of Gem Stone Identification*), but it would certainly be an esoteric thing to do.

Least interesting perhaps are the spots and fractures, unless the fracture is filled with air or liquid or subsequently introduced crystalline material. Then the result may be beautiful, like iris quartz, which is iridescent and colorful and is quite simply rock crystal with water-filled inclusions.

As you look at a flawed crystal through a microscope a whole new world of design opens up. The fine rutile needles called silk often show up, particularly in rubies, and sapphires—where it can actually improve the shade. Under a microscope the stone looks as if a skein of delicate silk had blown through it.

The rare demantoid garnet has a flaw all its own which is used as an identification mark: a curved plume of hair-thin lines, as graceful as those in the tail of a steed on some Greek intaglio. The "flaw," unsurprisingly enough, is called a horse's tail. The topaz has a teardrop for its flaw, and sometimes a centipede strolls through a moonstone.

A kind of geo-flaw law exists for many stones. In Africa crystals of zircon can be found within a diamond, but in Brazilian diamonds this never occurs. In Ceylon metamict zircons are often surrounded by a halo, not only in the local corundum but in spinels and garnets too. Very often aquamarines have perfect little crystal snowflakes as inclusions, so exquisite under the microscope one would be tempted to turn the aquamarine inside out.

Emeralds perhaps have the most fascinating flaws of all, which is just as well, for the unflawed emerald of any size is so rare as to be practically nonexistent. If these inclusions mar the emerald from the jeweler's point of view, they at least make an interesting job of it and are often called the emerald's "jardin." Sometimes a small, perfect cloud floats in its own green atmosphere, looking as if one could blow it away. This fragile little breath of a flaw may have been fixed in the emerald for billions of years. Sometimes an emerald has a three-phase inclusion. It holds within itself a tiny liquid lake. Sometimes within that lake a crystal floats, and within the crystal another lake, and within that lake perhaps another crystal, too small to see, yet existing as unseen stars do in the sky.

Green demantoid garnet with horse's tail.

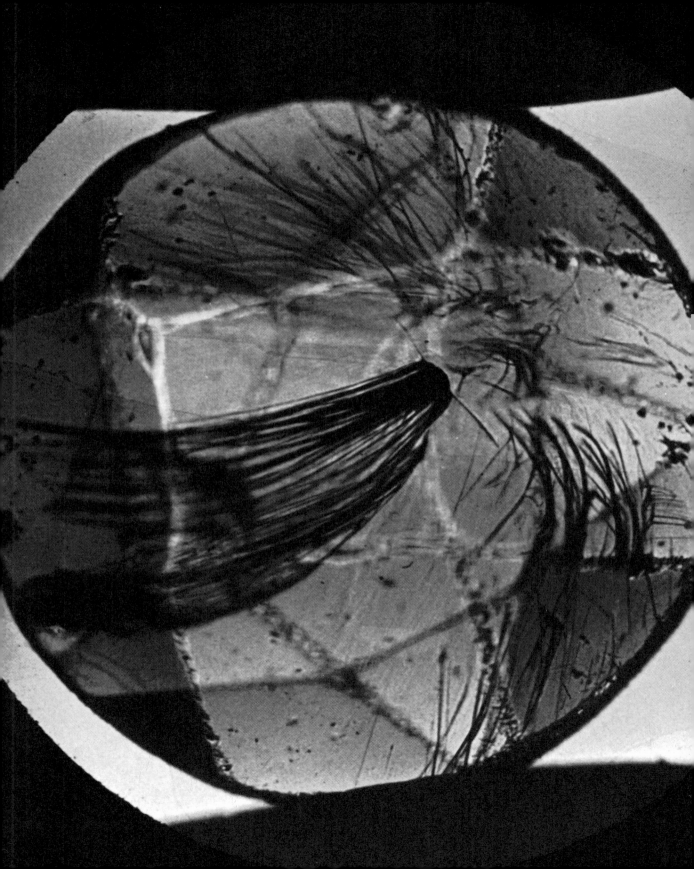

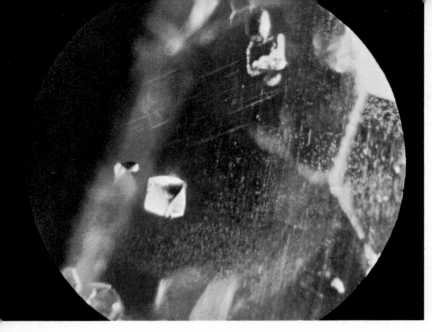

Two more photographs of flaws: (*Left*:) The emerald's "jardin," showing a three-phase inclusion. (*Below*:) Rutile needles which can create a "star" in a stone.

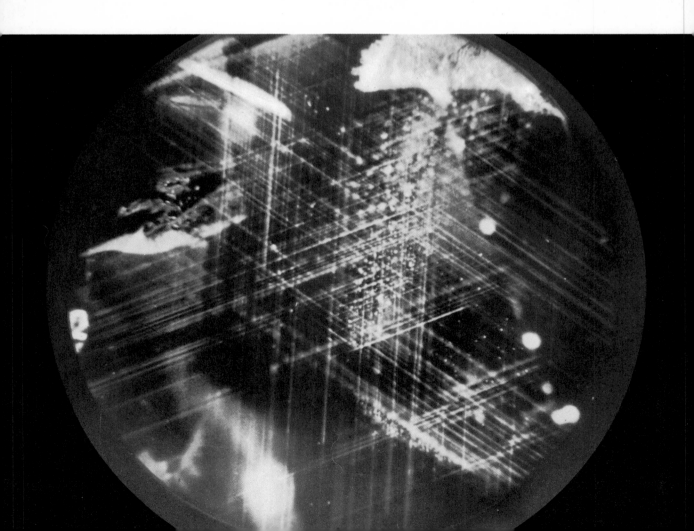

eat-treatment is a beauty treatment. It doesn't make the stone any better or worse, only more beautiful. It is a jeweler's way of doing something that nature might have done—and often does—but in some cases didn't.

Heat-treating rearranges the atoms, not of the crystal but of the pigmenting agent in the crystal. The results, depending upon the stone, the degree of heat, and sometimes upon the atmosphere, are spectacular and many. Heat can render a colored stone colorless. It can change the color of a crystal completely. It can improve the shade of a given color. It can lighten, but never darken.

Heating a stone is a more or less natural act because heat is natural. It is not at all like dyeing a stone or coating it, or coloring the lower part of the stone or the inside of a setting, as was so often done in earlier times. An enormous number of stones have been heat-treated and enormously improved by it. The only weakness in some heat-treated stones is a tendency to fade and return to their original color.

Perhaps the most spectacular examples of heat-treating are the blue zircon and the pink topaz, both of which hardly ever exist in nature. (See Chapters XXIV and XXVII.) There is a greenish beryl which can be heated to a clear blue aquamarine, and a certain type of blue tourmaline can be turned a bright emerald green. And in experienced hands streaky rubies and amethysts can be vastly improved.

HABIT

ost precious stones are crystals, and crystals are extraordinary in the neatness and precision of their growth. The "habit" of a crystal is its unvarying form: a polyhedron bounded by natural plane surfaces. The natural plane's surfaces are an outward expression of a definite internal ordered arrangement—or call it inner grace. Directional forces within the crystal establish the habit. (If a crystal had no directional force it would invariably end up as a sphere.) Though a crystal may grow to gigantic size, weighing a hundred tons or more, its habit is identical with that of its quarter-ounce sister. Such is the order of the nether world.

The most perfect crystals are produced by an even flow of the mother solution. There are distortions, of course; small inclusions, dust, water, air, crowding by adjoining stones, almost anything can throw the structure off, but, no matter what, the habit struggles to remain the same and carry out its original orders.

For all the similarity of habit in crystals, they are not automatons. When it comes to color, regimentation breaks down and the personality of the individual crystal begins to show. In the case of the tourmaline, regimentation not only breaks down but goes

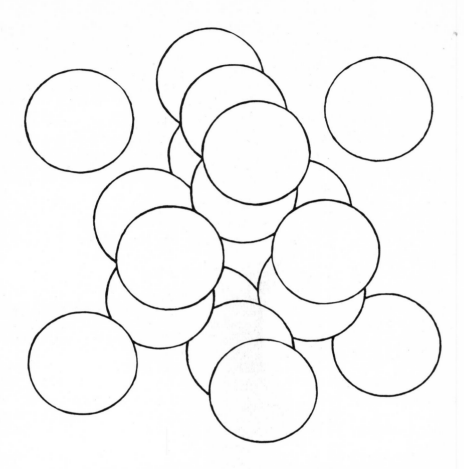

Atomic structure of a portion of a diamond, showing carbon atoms which bond together to produce its extreme hardness.

entirely to pieces in a most delightful and irresponsible way: changing color in mid-crystal, starting out one color and then covering itself completely with another, or deciding halfway through that perhaps, after all, it won't have any color. Even when it decides to be a green tourmaline the range can run (and sometimes in one crystal) from a dark syrupy green to geranium leaf, to parakeet, to an old and tired pistachio nut all within a single crystal. Opal can be all white and bland as an egg, an explosion of the spectrum in a midnight sky, or a flaring orange. An emerald can be as washed-out and dull as a dry corn husk or as darkly brilliant as some imagined holy lake at the back of the east wind. A single crystal can be a ruby at one end and a sapphire at the other. Some colors fade in the sun, some change color with heat—all of which shows crystals are not unresponsive.

Sometimes one finds a crystal formed around another crystal, and a beautiful and fanciful thing it can be: a blue tourmaline caught in rock crystal; a fragile-looking pink beryl surrounded by a pale-green tourmaline; blazing green malachite swirling its petticoats of Bibb lettuce in a slab of bright-blue azurite.

There are only about three thousand known mineral species, and if that sounds like a lot, consider the chemical family: there are close to half a million carbon compounds alone! We are not concerned, however, with even a fraction of that number, for ours is a very exclusive, limited field. Just for the record: more than half the earth's crust is made of the feldspars, which as a group house, among a multitude of other things, the lively green amazonite, labradorite with its opal-like play that was dear to the heart of Fabergé, the rare, clear, transparent lemon-yellow crystal called orthoclase, and its silvery celestial sister, the moonstone.

Next comes quartz, the most common single mineral in the earth's crust: splendid, colorful, and plentiful, and sometimes called by mineralogists the "tramp" as it soars, creeps, slithers, and manages to insert itself in the most unlikely places. Crystalline quartz includes the amethyst, citrine, cairngorm, rock crystal, and all the lovely gentle quartzes, such as rose quartz and gold quartz. More highly prized as gems by the ancients than by us is the large cryptocrystalline quartz family: chalcedony, carnelian, chrysoprase, agate, bloodstone, onyx, sardonyx, jasper, and so on. These are the familiar stones of the Bible and the Babylonians, the Egyptians and the Greeks.

The next division is pyroxene and amphibole, which are of interest only because pyroxene contains jadeite and spodumene, and amphibole contains nephrite, the other form of jade.

These three groups represent ninety per cent of the earth's crust. Of the remaining ten per cent, give nine per cent to olivine, zircon, all six varieties of garnet, corundum, tourmaline, and spinel.

The last remaining one per cent contains all the other gem material. Of course the number of gems found in these great divisions is minuscule, and the number worth cutting and polishing a tiny fraction of that minuscule.

These are the hard facts of precious stones—their ethnic divisions, one might say, but there is something "other" and rather intangible about precious stones. Just as a person can never be truly known by reducing him to his chemical components, so it is with precious stones. They warrant a bit more than physical definition. Yet some descriptive order must be maintained in the rambling realm of beauty, romance, metaphysics, color, and personal taste. If one were to line up the qualities essential to a "gem," they might be: beauty, durability, scarcity—and sometimes portability and fashion.

Beauty

V

One might assume that beauty at least is self-explanatory, but keeping in mind *"de gustibus"* and the "eye of the beholder," we should make some further attempt to list the qualities a gem must possess to call itself a beauty: transparency, luster, color, brilliance, and fire. Ideally it would have all five, in which case a colored diamond, called inelegantly a "fancy," would fit the bill precisely. A turquoise, on the other hand, relies entirely on color and luster, and when the shade is fine might appear more beautiful than a stone with fire but poor color.

Most precious stones are transparent. The measure of a crystal's transparency is its ability to transmit light, and not necessarily its ability to be "seen through." The diamond has it, and so has rock crystal. The sapphire has it, but not the opal. If a stone transmits light weakly it is translucent, as with some jade, some chrysoberyl, and amber and the like. When—as with turquoise, coral, or malachite, for instance—a stone doesn't transmit light at all it is called opaque.

In all translucent and opaque stones, luster is of paramount importance. It describes how the *surface* of a stone appears. There are many kinds of luster:

Adamantine describes the fine, hard, adamant luster of a diamond most exactly.

Vitreous describes the glassy luster of emeralds and quartz.

Greasy is accurate, too, and applies to those stones which look as if they had been lightly slicked with oil or have a metallic sheen: for example, opal and lapis lazuli.

Pearly luster is just that.

Silky is precisely the right term for the surface look of some chrysoberyl, malachite, and white satin spar.

Dull is not a frequent luster in the world of gems; it well describes the soft matte finish of coral.

Some stones depend entirely on color for their high place in the hierarchy. At the same time, color is the loosest definition of all, and it has to be. "A fine blue stone" is a meaningless phrase, whereas such words as fire, brilliance, transparency, and adamantine luster are precise.

26

All gems are either allochromatic or idiochromatic. In the idiochromatic group the element which pigments the stone is an intrinsic part of the stone's chemistry. Lapis lazuli and malachite are good examples. Most gems, however, are allochromatic, which means that when they are "pure" they are colorless. The color in almost all of the beautiful gems is due to impurities. A trace of chromium, for instance, which really has no business being there, is what gives the emerald its green and, oddly enough, the ruby its red. An intrusion of iron and titanium turns the aquamarine blue.

Sometimes the coloring agent permeates the entire crystal, which is a splendid state of affairs, resulting in a superb, evenly colored stone. Usually, however, the trace is unevenly spread in the crystal, leaving patches or sections or even layers of crystal either palely pigmented or completely colorless. Sometimes several quite different colors will be present in one crystal, indicating that other pigmenting agents entered the crystal while it was still being formed.

Tone is a division of color. It carries one color up or down the scale, so to speak. It describes the lighter and darker version of the same stone, for crystals of the same family, and even a crystal itself, can vary enormously; also, if two stones are cut from one evenly pigmented crystal, the twenty-carat stone will appear to be deeper, darker, perhaps brighter—practically another color—than the three-carat stone.

Tone also describes the magnitude or intensity of color. Some colors reach out across a crowded room. They leap bright and clear as lance tips from their settings. A good turquoise can do this, and Imperial jade, the orange sapphire, and some emeralds. Other stones, such as rubies, sapphires, amethysts, and opals, or the very velvetiest peridot, have to be seen close up to be appreciated.

The permanence of a stone's color may have something to do with man's devotion to it. Most things of equivalently beautiful color are either soft, or perishable, or changeable. A flower, silk, a peach are sadly mortal. A particularly heart-catching sunrise comes once and never again. The sea is every shade at every moment. Only the stone—with few exceptions—holds its color, true and unchanging, forever lasting.

Brilliance is the dazzle, the sparkle, the twinkle of a stone, a quality which depends almost entirely on cutting, but, as with fire, the potential must be in the stone. The best cutter in the world cannot produce the degree of brilliance in a piece of rock crystal or colorless beryl or topaz that he can in a diamond. Brilliance describes the amount of light reflected *back* from the stone, and that in turn depends on both the stone's refractive indices and its hardness. Transparency is, of course, essential, for no opaque stone can show brilliance. Sometimes brilliance and fire go hand in hand, which is a spectacular show, but, barring the diamond and two or three others, it is infrequent.

Fire sets a stone in direct kinship with light itself, but the intrinsic quality must be in the stone to begin with. Even so, until the stone is cut in a certain exact and mathematical way, no fire will show. Even the diamond—that very bonfire of light—could show no fire until the understanding of refractive indices developed in the seventeenth century. (See Chapter XIII.) Fire is achieved when light enters one facet, bounces off a facet in the lower part of the stone (the pavilion), and emerges through a facet *not* parallel with the facet it entered. In this way the light is bent and breaks up into the spectrum colors, which is why, when you turn a diamond in the light, it flashes with sparks of red, orange, yellow, green, blue, indigo, and violet.

Light dispersion within the stone is what makes fire possible, and the degree of dispersion varies sharply. The sphene and the diamond stand well at the top of the list of gems, with the rare green demantoid garnet hard on their heels, and zircon next in line. Lustrous and even brilliant as they may be, the ruby, sapphire, and emerald show no fire.

Some stones, while not showing fire, have a play called dichroism. Here, as the stone is turned in the light, two colors break free instead of the whole spectrum. The ruby, for instance, can send out bright little sparks of two shades of red; the amethyst can fire off red and violet sparks; the sapphire, kunzite, pink tourmaline, emerald, pink topaz, purple and green corundum, for instance, all show dichroism.

Whether we know it or not, there is always a certain amount of pressure from various sources to "persuade" us toward one stone or another. There is nothing wrong in listening to these persuasions, unless we allow them to rob us of our own tastes. We have all felt them. One has been made to feel that it is almost irreverent not to love an emerald. A half-carat, off-color diamond has somehow taken precedence as an engagement ring over a far lovelier sparkling pink tourmaline, or the murmuring softness of a peridot of a handsome number of carats. Then fashion nudges us toward a certain stone, and, after having loathed it since childhood, one begins to think, "Well, maybe it has a certain charm after all." When one has been told and told that the ruby is enormously valuable and so obviously must be beautiful, one may acquiesce, weakly avoiding the fact that one has never liked red in any of its shades. There is every virtue in acquiring a new taste, but never in letting an old and essential one go.

Somewhere along the line we lost our innocence about stones. Once upon a time we may have taken a more wide-eyed pleasure in a crystal: the delightful discovery, the playful handling, holding it up to the sun, cupping it in a palm, and then possibly laying it aside and forgetting it. But that was then, if ever such a "then" existed. Now, even for stone-lovers, it is almost impossible to feel "freely" about precious stones: free of the awareness of their price, free of covetousness, insurance premiums, fashion; free of the usage of stones to convey messages of status, wealth, superiority, or as a highly visible evaluation of one's charms.

St. Eloi, patron saint of goldsmiths, and affianced couple. Painting by P. Christus, fifteenth century.

Durability

VI

Durability in some degree is certainly essential to a gem. It measures not only the hardness of the stone but its unscratchableness, its ability to take a high polish, its strength to withstand damage. In fact, durability measures a stone's ability to survive —beautifully.

There are some grand old yardsticks for measuring hardness that are still in use today. The stones range themselves into those which can be scratched by a fingernail, a copper coin, a knife blade, a piece of window glass, and a steel file. Though not highly accurate, these yardsticks at least establish ratios.

The table of hardness used by most jewelers, however, is called the Mohs scale, worked out in the early nineteenth century by Friedrich Mohs. In this scale, one stone is measured directly against another, and all are arranged in order of hardness. Each stone can scratch the one below it and be scratched by the one above. One might say it establishes a kind of pecking order among gems.

The Mohs rule of thumb doesn't pretend to be rigid or precise, but when two stones closely resemble each other—a mediocre ruby and a fine spinel, for instance— the scale will tell which is which. The Mohs scale doesn't, however, show a stone's brittleness or the presence of fractures or cleavages, or the variations of hardness on the different faces of a single crystal, nor does it make allowance for subtleties. Stones of the same variety can vary a little. The diamonds of Borneo and New South Wales, for instance, are apparently harder than South African diamonds because of their gnarled structure. Ceylon sapphires are harder than rubies, Kashmir sapphires slightly softer. The difference, however, is less than minuscule. The scale goes like this: 10: Diamond. 9: Corundum. 8: Topaz. 7: Quartz. 6: Orthoclase. 5: Apatite. 4: Fluorite. 3: Calcite. 2: Gypsum. 1: Talc.

10. The diamond stands alone with a number all to itself. It is many times harder than the stones immediately below it, and none can scratch it. In fact, some black diamonds are so hard that they cannot even be polished, let alone cut, even by another diamond. Just such obdurate characters are the uncleavable Black Diamonds of Bahai.

9. Corundum is the family name of the ruby, sapphire, and those lovely colorful

corundum crystals often quite wrongly called "Oriental" topaz, emerald, and amethyst.

Between 9 and 8 comes the chrysoberyl group, to which alexandrite and Oriental cat's-eye belong.

8. At this stage of hardness are the spinels, most of the beryls—which include the emerald, aquamarine, morganite, and the golden beryl—and topaz.

7. This stage includes zircons, tourmalines, and the whole great quartz family, chief among them being the amethyst, citrine, and cairngorm.

It is here on the Mohs scale of hardness that the discussion begins as to which are the precious and semi-precious stones. Edward Streeter, Robert Shipley, and Robert Webster, for instance, all accepted experts, insist that there is no distinct dividing line. One might grade stones, but to separate them arbitrarily is not wise. Shipley suggests that they all be called "gemstones." Edward Streeter made five divisions but insisted that they were all "precious." With a perfectly straight face he started pearl at I, which must have shocked a number of new young mineralogists who might have just stopped themselves in time from telling the Great Man, "Pearl, sir, is organic. . . ." He placed the ruby at II, ahead of the diamond at III. At IV he placed sapphire, Oriental cat's-eye, and precious opal; and at V he placed alexandrite, jacinth, Oriental onyx, peridot, topaz, and zircon. However one expert, a specialist named Julius Wodiska, took sharp exception to this and gently hinted that Mr. Streeter's judgment was not entirely unbiased. He suggested that when Streeter placed the diamond at only III, the Syndicate in London was not yet in control of the South African diamond output, while Burma, with its glorious rubies, *was* under England's control. At about the same time, a German expert called K.-E. Kluge made his divisions of I diamond, II corundum, III chrysoberyl, and IV spinel.

If you choose to go along with the idea that anything quartz (7) can scratch should not belong to the club, then you must argue with the great Mr. Streeter and, what's more, you must disallow the rapturous turquoise, the fiery bright demantoid garnet, and the most dazzling opal. For all at sixes and sevens on the Mohs scale (and some at considerably less) are the clear-water peridot, the most imperial jade, bright blue zircon, sparkling pink kunzite, to mention only a few. And if one is going to use this sharp division, what can one say about precious angel-skin coral at only 3½, and pearls which vacillate mostly between 2½ and 3½, which Streeter places as the most precious of all precious things?

Semiprecious is of course a silly phrase, like semidead or semipregnant. They are *all* precious. The fact that some are softer and more perishable than others does not render them less beautiful—or precious. Certainly the softer stones must be protected and cherished, but then one doesn't leave a Queen Anne commode out in the rain, or put wet glasses on a Verney Martin box. Ideally, softer stones should not be worn as rings or bracelets where they are most likely to be banged and scratched. Earrings, pins, and necklaces keep them safe. There are many soft historic stones about to show that given a modicum of protection, they can be as long-lasting as their harder cousins.

This deep concern over softness, unscratchableness, seems to belabor only one aspect of durability. Apparently it does not include the fact that some gems may crack and break on a hard, unyielding surface; that others, at a sharp rap, can start flaws or "feathers"; that the most alive-looking opals can dry out, wither, or shatter. Some stones fracture invisibly and are actually held together by the setting. When such stones are taken out to be repolished or reset, they fall apart in the hands of the dismayed jeweler, and this, one should know, is *not* his fault or responsibility.

Only the diamond, to all intents and purposes, is invincible and has perhaps set an impossible standard for all other stones. But even some of the hardest stones, including the diamond, have what are called "cleavage planes." This means that, if you give even a hard stone a great whack or drop it on a rigid surface at a certain angle, it may conceivably break along the cleavage line. It is rare, but it can happen, which is one reason why the so-called hardness of stones can give a false impression. There is this to be said for the softer stones: while you can snap or shatter a cracker—you can't break butter.

The durability of stones has a more fascinating aspect than mere imperviousness. Marred, scratched, chipped, flawed, or even broken, in relation to us stones are immortal. They do not die. Gems of incredible antiquity are here, present and visible, to link us tightly to the past in much the same way as the "hand that shook the hand that shook Washington's" does. Today you can lay your palm on the very sapphire that lay so often under the fingers of Charlemagne. You can hold in your hand and exchange glances with a staring malevolent eye agate that may have frightened our first grandfather out of his superstitious wits. You could slide on your finger the Black Prince's ruby ring, a jewel he dearly loved.

Another reason for the durability of stones is that man is intensely practical. By and large man seems always to have known the value of a fine stone, and so in his own way he has carefully protected it. Through ignorance paintings have been defaced, murals and mosaics whitewashed, Leonardo's great plaster equestrian study, the Sforza Colossus, was allowed to rot in the rain and become a target for idle soldiers, but stones were apparently known and valued by the most ignorant. Hidden in dark places, repatriated, reset, renamed, they turned up again and again, and the great ones such as the Hope Diamond, which had even been cut into three pieces, were recognized and their value kept intact if not augmented.

If stones were not durable, we would never know certain revealing things about the taste of a particular era: that the Franks used such a delicate pastel palette: chalky pink, pale whited-green, misty blue, and cool light beige for their rough round beads. One might have expected harsher, brasher colors, even from the sixth-century French. If the colors of the gems didn't remain true, and, if one couldn't see in many a museum and collection bright garnets or dark carnelian played against turquoise, one might think it a daring modern combination instead of seventh-century Lombardian taste; that the four-thousand-year-old Egyptian fashion for bright blue glass with emerald-green feldspar could have been born yesterday, or tomorrow, and that the eye of Alexander the Great delighted in pale, cool emeralds and smooth, dark, smoldering garnets.

While the entombed silk and linen can shimmer into dust when it meets the sudden air of today, and scrolls of papyrus can splinter and crack, the bright polished gems travel through the millennia unchanged, unfaded, and unperturbed.

Scarcity

VII

Scarcity is self-explanatory, but scarcity alone doesn't make a gem. It is the fact that beauty and durability are scarce. A ton of beryl or corundum or olivine may be unearthed without turning up even one crystal worth calling a gem.

Another form of scarce is "rare." Blue and green diamonds are so very rare that "scarce" isn't a tight enough word to hold them. Pigeon-blood rubies, unmarred by silk, of over three or four carats are close to nonexistent, and unflawed emeralds of splendid color of over five or six carats practically never form.

There are green garnets, which because they occur infrequently have many many times the value of even the most beautiful rose-red garnets—which occur all over the world and are anything but scarce. There is benitoite (found only in California) in superb blue and violet crystals, but discovered so recently that it has not had a chance to get itself properly established with a solid reputation. As it is also very scarce, this may never happen, for a stone must have a certain availability to have value.

Some stones are scarce for political reasons. Practically no jadeite is reaching the United States from Burma. The beautiful emerald-green alexandrite is not coming out of Russia, and for some reason the large black opals of Australia are hard to find.

Scarce, within the category of beautiful and durable stones, is the Beautiful Example. The diamond of incredible purity or color is one. The uvarovite (green) garnet of over half a carat; the big, bright, flawless red tourmaline. Sapphires are far from scarce and can grow to a very good size, but rare indeed are large crystals of that shade called Kashmir blue, an almost fourth-dimensional color. It is usually described as a cornflower blue with both brilliance and softness and a depth that gives one the feeling that one could proceed straight down into it for a hundred velvety miles.

There is another kind of scarcity which is entirely man-made. It is the scarcity of those stones, known and recorded in literature and inventories, clearly rendered in old paintings, stones known to have rested on the very flesh of history. As the stones themselves are durable, they continue to exist—somewhere. But where? Where is the great table diamond, the Mirror of Portugal? Where are the balas rubies of the "Three Brethren," the great brooch of Henry VIII? Where is the mantle clasp of Alexander? Where

Jewelry design by Salvador Dali in collaboration with the Duc di Verdura.

are the sapphires and emeralds from the sixth-century crown of the Empress Theodolinda?

Theodolinda was the amazing queen who, through either charm or zeal, almost single-handed drew Lombardy away from the Aryan heresy and back to the Mother Church. If the crown was to Theodolinda's taste, she had style, a fine restrained kind of elegance, and a passion for blue and green. No modern jeweler could produce a more charming object than the little crown so precisely studded with emeralds, sapphires, and half-pearls. The crown is there, still to be seen in Monza, Italy but the stones aren't. In 1797 Napoleon took Theodolinda's crown from Monza, where it had been for more than a thousand years, and put it in the Bibliothèque Nationale in Paris, for "safekeeping." Safe in those hallowed halls, the emeralds, sapphires, and the pearls (all but one) were quietly removed and replaced with the Very Best Glass, and mother-of-pearl. Napoleon's efforts to preserve antiquities was not a marked success, but the crown is back at Monza, bereft of all but its historical value. The stones are scattered who knows where, but they almost certainly exist.

When one considers the works of man: wars, plunder, and thefts, it's a wonder that so many of the great historical stones are still visible. The fact that they are we owe to several things.

We owe it first to the Sumerians, Egyptians, and other early peoples for burying fine gems with their noble dead. We owe it to prehistoric man for placing with his departed chief amulets or treasures of beads or quartz.

Conversely, we owe thanks to Charlemagne for *forbidding* the burying of precious things with the dead on the grounds that (and this has a strangely contemporary ring) it took too much wealth out of circulation. Thanks to him we don't have to dig for *every* early European stone.

Perhaps we owe thanks to the enterprising European traders who traveled in the East and brought back the historic stones. From the twelfth and thirteenth centuries on, Europeans began to go quite marvelously mad on the subject of precious stones. Between Marco Polo and the Crusaders, such tales and stones came back from the East as to make the most sophisticated baron's eyes bulge. It was shortly after that that he began to become disenchanted with his previously treasured "balas rubies," "carbuncles," and "hyacinths" or, to give them today's names, his spinels, garnets, and zircons.

Prior to this time, when a European country or ruler was short of gold, or had lost a battle, or wished to be ingratiating with some power, or prevent a war, lands, his castles, and often his sons and daughters were used as bargaining power. In the East for centuries men had used gems for the identical purposes, and it was a method the European now adopted. In the twelfth century a ruler might put his gold throne in pawn, but think of the risk of the high visibility, the cartage and effort compared to slipping a hundred-carat stone into the heel of a boot.

Charlemagne, painted by Albrecht Dürer, wearing the crown of the Holy Roman Empire, now displayed as the German Imperial crown at the Treasury in Vienna.

karolus impat

magnus Annus 14·

During the following centuries a horde of great stones, mostly diamonds, poured into Europe (not even a fraction of the horde that remained in the East, however), where they commanded great strapping prices. By the sixteenth century it would be hard to find a safer investment, once the stone was safely out of India and into the strongbox. As in the East, gems were not necessarily for adornment. They were money. They were given as security for goods or for a life. They changed the course of a war, raised regiments, equipped cavalry. They were used as dowries, as ransom, as gifts to impress or intimidate a visiting king, and of course as bribes. Catherine de' Medici offered the finest stone of France to Elizabeth I of England in exchange for Calais, and, although she was refused, it may have been a near thing, for, deeply as Elizabeth loved her England, her passion for jewels was a close second. Gems traded hands and countries, and many of them were known to half Europe. By the seventeenth century a great number had, by hook or crook, gathered themselves in England to join the already historic (if not great) stones of the crown, and the truly notable ones collected by Henry VIII and Elizabeth and James I.

Then, as if there were a kind of balance wheel in the affairs of great collections, came the great scattering of the historic stones of England. Many that Henrietta Maria didn't smuggle out or Royalists conceal, thieves stole or Roundheads—displaying more stupidity than they are usually credited with—destroyed. They trampled them, burned them, put them to the hammer—for such is the way of the zealot—ignoring the fact that the stones could have been sold or pawned to finance their new republic. Silver and gold they melted down for coin, but in a fervor of hatred the regalia, the very relics

This pendant, the Three Brethren, has three large table-cut balas rubies (red spinels), four pearls, and a diamond said to be the first one cut by de Berquem. After it was taken from Charles the Bold, Duke of Burgundy, at the battle of Granson in 1475, it came into the possession of Henry VIII, Queen Mary I, Charles I, and Queen Henrietta Maria. Its final fate is unknown.

Oliver Cromwell, the Protector, under whose protection most of the crown jewels of England were disbanded, destroyed, or melted down for coin.

of England, the stones which had been intimate with the formation of the country, were destroyed or vanished. But not all of them vanished forever.

In addition to the few things hidden by Royalists or taken out of the country, some were redeemed from Holland, but when Charles II came back for the Restoration the cupboard was, to put it mildly, bare. The King found only a few battered and tarnished silver gilt frames for crowns, empty of stones and obviously considered not worth even melting down for metal. He chose a frame that, one supposes, fitted him best, hired stones from the local jewelers for five hundred pounds, and wore the crown for his coronation. There is a small irony here. Later it was discovered that the crown he wore was very likely Oliver Cromwell's!

Be it said of the Protector he didn't *want* to be King and certainly didn't want a crown. Yet there was a large party in favor of his having one, and a crown was made, some say, from an old empty Tudor frame. After the Protector died and was laid out in state at Somerset House, the crown was there beside him on the chair of State.

Another kind of scarcity one might attribute (half seriously) to the therapeutic use of stones that started as long ago as the amulet did and continued right up to what one might call modern times. As late as 1757 one could go into a chemist's shop and buy powdered emerald or ruby, rock crystal or lapis lazuli and dose oneself. Most of the remedies can be traced back to the planetary-stone time, for, along with a stone and a metal, each planet controlled or governed certain parts of the body. During the Renaissance precious stones were used as condiments in Italy—but sparingly, one imagines.

VIII

Portability

Through history no refugee has needed to be reminded of the value that lies in the easy portability of stones. Stones are small and easily concealed, and have a remarkably steady value in the capitals of the world. Uncountable times a stone has made possible a new life in a new country. There is a great jeweler in New York who, to this day, buys a single diamond every year from a refugee of the 1917 Russian Revolution. Who knows how many refugees left Germany in the early thirties, carrying stones?

Because of the combination of portability and fairly steady value, all through history great stones have worked hard for their living. Sometimes smuggled, sometimes taken openly to Holland, to France, to Switzerland, they have changed the course of a war and the destinies of human beings. Queen Henrietta Maria was able to smuggle to France enough of the crown jewels of England to raise powder, carbines, and coin for her beleaguered husband, Charles I. The Sancy Diamond raised money steadily from the time of Henry III of France right up to, and through, the Revolution. The Pitt Diamond (which is now called the Regent and can be seen at the Louvre but which originally belonged to the grandfather of William Pitt) was pawned as late as 1790 for cavalry equipment, and again raised money in 1798, contributing directly to Napoleon's victory at Marengo. The three great "balas rubies" of France—the Côte de Bretagne, the Roman A, and the Oeuf de Naples—were constantly going back and forth on one financial rescue mission or another. The Peacock Throne has many times the value of even an enormous stone, but one couldn't swallow it, or put it in a pocket or the heel of a boot.

Of course, the negative side is that even the handsomest jewel is comparatively small, and as a consequence, easy to steal. Stones can be cut in a way that can make their identity unrecognizable to the average person, but there is always the knowledgeable buyer.

One tale which combines the ludicrous with the macabre and ends up an *opéra bouffe* is the story of the "escape" of the Hanoverian crown jewels. George V, the sad blinded son of Ernest Augustus, was King of Hanover when the Prussians swept down on him in 1866. King George was hurried away, but so swift was the descent that the

The Côte de Bretagne, a large and splendid red spinel, belonged to Anne de Bretagne. In the eighteenth century it was carved into a dragon and hung in an Order.

crown jewels and all the crown plate were still in the palace when the enemy arrived. Whatever their personal politics, the members of the palace staff were united in one thing: hatred of the Prussians. Right under the noses of the occupying forces, with Prussian sentries at every door, they managed to pack into empty wine barrels not only a number of the crown jewels but also the great gold and silver dinner service for two thousand, and smuggle the barrels (clanking softly, one imagines) out through an old half-forgotten subterranean passage that led to a church. At the time, the church was tenanted by a wine merchant, a fact glossed over rather lightly by contemporary accounts, but the wine merchant, a loyalist too, received the barrels and, mixing them with other barrels containing the real thing, shipped them out by rail to Vienna and England by boat.

Meanwhile, back at the palace, the Lord Chamberlain and his wife, who was Mistress of the Robes, managed to slip out the rest of the crown jewels and the Queen's personal jewels. First they were buried in a corner of the Lord Chamberlain's garden, but not for long. Whether some intelligence reached the Lord Chamberlain or whether he was given to intuitions, he decided that the garden was not a safe enough hiding place, and so once again, by stealth and in darkness, the jewels were gathered up—crowns, scepters, state swords as well. With the treasures fastened into the linings of great heavy winter mantles, the conspirators flitted silently to the Ducal vaults. One by one the great stone sarcophagus lids were pried open to find those which were the most accommodating. No one dared to disturb the sacred remains of the Electress Sophia, and in other cases the sarcophagus too closely fit the man, but finally one great lid lifted to reveal only the pitiful little corpse of a stillborn child—and in this spaciousness the crown jewels were laid. Separately, the Queen's personal jewels were fitted into the tomb of a young electoral prince, and here they remained for several years, even though the Prussians, deeply chagrined at the loss of the treasure, posted a high reward for their recovery. Of all the hundreds of people involved in the secret of the jewels not one stepped forward to claim it.

With the threat of another war, King George decided that the jewels must somehow be removed from Hanover and taken to the safety of England. Once more, the jewels were surreptitiously smuggled out of the Ducal vaults—but this time they went to a picnic. The large items were put in picnic baskets, the crown occupied a kind of glorified sponge bag, the swords went into gun cases and the smaller items were variously in the pockets and coattails of the jolly rustics whose hilarity and laughter hid any possible clatter and clinking. The merry coaching party set off, with only one member limping slightly from a case of State-Sword-down-the-trouser-leg, for they were one gun case shy.

Deep in the woods they stopped at a forester's cottage, and there they were met by the doughty Countess Kielmansegge and other ladies of the erstwhile court, switching their great skirts, tilting their parasols, screaming at ants for the benefit of any possible observer. One by one the ladies vanished into the cottage, there to sew in the lining of a dress a great necklace, to hide in bodices huge orders and brooches (which must have left bas-reliefs on their skin for days to come) ; tiaras, one imagines, were worked into bustles, bracelets concealed under sleeves, and rings looped onto pins inside a skirt. An extra gun case was found to relieve the limper and the ladies were ready for the long trip by train to Vienna, where suddenly the Hanoverian crown was remembered. It was large and heavy and, to put it mildly, wouldn't fold. It was then that the Countess Kielmansegge had her inspiration. She settled the monstrous crown on her head and tied over it her fetching black lace bonnet. Sturdy monarchs had complained of its weight, but smiling and nodding and holding her little head proudly, she wore it all the way to Vienna without displaying a trace of the agony she must have suffered.

A mid-fifteenth-century tale of portability seems to indicate that women have a curious knack for the inventive smuggling of precious objects, however large. Queen Elizabeth fled to Vienna with her infant son and the great Holy Crown turned upside down with a spoon in it—disguised as the baby's porringer. Those two efforts make single-stone smuggling look like child's play.

IX

Fashion

*W*hen the mind reacts to the word "fashion" it suddenly becomes very difficult to make a separation between fashions in jewelry and fashions in stones. To ease the effort, one might settle for one of Webster's definitions of fashion and stick to it: "favored at the time."

Fashion is a strange phenomenon which can neither be contained nor foreseen. Fashions in stones seem to have little to do with beauty or color or value. All at once a searchlight turns for a time on one particular stone, no better or worse than its fellows, and suddenly it becomes desirable to a number of people.

By and large, fashion should rest in impermanence. A fashion should come—and go. That puts one in an awkward position regarding emeralds, rubies, pearls, sapphires, and turquoises. They came—but they never went. Are they then subject to fashion? Could one say that shoes are in fashion, or breakfast? After something has been around for ten thousand years it is difficult to think of it as being suddenly "in" or a startling novelty.

It is hard to tell about the long, long ago pre-world-trade fashions (Sumerian, Babylonian, or Egyptian), whether a certain favored stone was a fashion—or simply available. Oddly enough, to be fashionable a stone must have a certain prevalence and availability. A stone, when it is too rare or too expensive, becomes a novelty, a marvel, a curiosity, a lovely or lamentable oddity—but not a fashion.

Has the ruby, for instance, ever been what one would call a fashion? Coveted, revered, it is too scarce and too expensive to be available, but even in the rarefied world of those who can buy rubies there is a certain ebb and flow in its fashionableness. One year emeralds will have a slight edge, another year sapphires, then rubies will glide back into first place again. For reasons perhaps of pure scarcity, the demantoid garnet has never been fashion, nor have blue and green diamonds. One can suit oneself as to the semantics here, saying either that the ruby, emerald, etc., have never been in fashion, or that they are above fashion.

One stone which has been completely and inarguably "in" for maybe eight thousand years is the turquoise. Other stones have swept in and out, but that strange, smiling stone continues imperturbably nodding politely to the newcomers, waving them good-by, absolutely confident that it is a fashion immortal. It has been used grandly, casually, religiously. Sometimes it has been conspicuously in fashion: set with diamonds in great Edwardian tiaras or late Georgian necklaces; or favored in medieval times in its almost apple-green version, used to inlay thrones or a cigarette box; set casually with coral, as it was in the twenties; or, as of now, set usually in gold—which is just about where it started out so many thousands of years ago—or surrounded by diamonds.

Pearls, perhaps, are an immortal fashion. Since the moment they were first pierced they had no ups or downs. In fact, whether rosy orientals, creamy cultured, or luminous imitations, as a fashion they seem as permanently "in" as food and water. On occasion in fashion history they have been combined with colored stones: rimming a tenth-century crown of spinels, amethysts, and topazes; hanging from the brilliant stone and enamel brooches and pendants of the Renaissance; mixed with rubies in great Tudor necklaces; threaded between emeralds in Egypt; bezel-set in sapphire bracelets in Byzantium—and again, in our own time, by Chanel.

Now it looks as if the diamond might become a permanent fashion too. It hasn't had anything like the time the pearl and the turquoise have to prove its standing, but the fact that one doesn't remember what a comparative late-comer the diamond is rather proves the point.

The garnet is a stone that has been repeatedly in and out of fashion. It started in the Bronze Age: garnet pebbles strung as necklaces. Whether it was a "fashion" is a question of whether fashion had been invented then. Next it turned up in Egyptian jewelry. It wasn't the sweeping fashion of turquoise, lapis lazuli, or green feldspar, but it was there and present. Then it came to the Greeks, and they obviously thought the "carbuncle" was a splendid stone with enormous chic. They used it constantly and importantly. It was usually either the dark pyrope or the purple-tinged almandine, and they set it in gold and often in a combination to make modern taste quail—with dark carnelian. There was also a fashion for cutting curved slivers of garnet and using it for inlay, as if it were enamel, which fashion the Romans took up for buckles, bracelets, and pins.

The garnet continued to smolder through the Dark and Middle Ages, a respected stone that glowed on crowns and pendants, but not à la mode, and rather on a par with coral, for in the thirteenth and fourteenth centuries it wasn't even mentioned in the English royal inventories. Slowly it vanished behind some curtain, only to reappear once more, and this time as a tremendous fashion, as the pyrope garnet parures of the Victorian era. Now it is in eclipse again, but with all that power of reviving itself, one wonders when next . . .

The peridot has never been a great fashion either, even for that brief moment when the green ones were thought to be emeralds. The precious topaz, on the other hand, has been a fashion and was also one of the mighty stones of antiquity—along with the amethyst, lapis lazuli, turquoise, zircon, olivine, emerald, and most of the cryptocrystal-

(*Left:*) Phoenician lady, wearing heavy necklaces and wheel ornaments studded with shells. (*Right:*) Etruscan lady, wearing fashionable earrings and necklace.

line quartz. As a fashion it has been a mild but not a very insistent one, which is just as well, for precious topaz is very rare. But it had a sudden vogue in the late eighteenth century and again in the nineteen-forties. However, most of what one sees in stores is quartz citrine.

Amethysts were in fashion from earliest times, though the Egyptians and the Greeks were far from exigent as to its color, and happily used pale and streaky crystals. In Europe it continued to be a very fashionable stone, and as it was often confused with purple corundum, it was set in jewelry with emeralds, rubies, and topaz—i.e., with precious stones. It lingered on the fringes of fashion (having entered the Church meanwhile) up to the eighteenth century and then shot up into high place again, possibly because of the discovery of the beautiful lively Siberian amethysts, and possibly because of the brilliant cut, which made it a very different stone from the big somber or pallid cabochons of Greek, medieval, and Renaissance times. Now the amethyst has drifted into quiet waters again, but as it is the only purple stone readily available, it will be needed again.

For more than a thousand years the beautiful, rosy "balas ruby" was a fashion. Table-cut or cabochon, it was a favorite from the time the Indians first unearthed it and continued as a great fashion in Europe until—in a case of the most shocking snobbery—it was discovered somewhere around the middle of this millennium that it wasn't

(*Left:*) A Capetian costume. Tenth century. (*Right:*) A lady of the Charles VI period, wearing horned headdress and heavy necklace. Fourteenth century.

a ruby at all, but a spinel, and for no better reason than that it was cast into oblivion, or nearly. When one looks at the great Renaissance and Tudor paintings, absolutely glowing with a profusion of spinels, one can't help wondering where they all are.

Opals have never been a big fashion, though they were much sought after in Roman times. They did have a slight flurry in the upper strata after the glorious black opals were discovered in Australia and Queen Victoria began handing them out to relatives and friends like peppermints.

"Portrait of a Lady" by Antonio Pollaiuolo, showing jewelled hair-bands and a simple necklace. Fifteenth century.

Marguerite de Valois. Sixteenth century.

One might almost say that during the Byzantine era, the alexandrine and during the Renaissance, precious stones themselves were out of fashion. They played a definitely secondary role in the extraordinary gold and enamel jewels and were accessories to the design. One can understand the almost total takeover of gold and enamel during the Renaissance when one recalls the goldsmiths: Ghiberti, Botticelli, Cellini, Luca della Robbia, Verrocchio in Italy, not to mention Dürer in Germany and Holbein in England, and all this while the stonecutter was limping along with primitive cuts (there wasn't much zest to a point-cut diamond and the table cut wasn't much livelier), and in fact the unfortunate lapidary wasn't even allowed into the guilds. Of course, rubies, emeralds, and sapphires continued to be cherished and used and to lend their color to the enamel to make a display of power and strength that suited admirably the opulent brocades and damasks of the day. (Anything less brilliant would have looked washed-out or invisible against such encrusted richness.) And it was during the Renaissance that the baroque pearl became a great fashion, its strange or distorted shape used with magical inventiveness to form the core of a design.

The tide turned in the mid-seventeenth century, and the haughty goldsmith found himeslf yielding place to the stonecutter. The rose cut had been invented, De Berquem had discovered surface reflection, and Peruzzi had unlocked the secret of light refraction. Fire had been born in the diamond and brilliance in many colored stones. Then the precious stones returned to fashion with a vengeance and were determined to shine alone. Enamel was still being used as settings, but now it was to extol the jewel, and soon it was a case of the less setting the better. By the time of Louis XV the palette too

(*Left:*) Mademoiselle de la Vallière. Seventeenth century.

Fashion in the eighteenth century.

had completely changed from the trumpeting of rubies, emeralds, and sapphires, to the clear soprano tones of pink and pale-yellow diamonds. By the end of the eighteenth century the topaz and amethyst were most heartily back in fashion, lending their gold and purple to great parures, usually set in gold.

And then again, briefly, during the Directoire, precious stones gave way to "jewelry": to the long dangling earrings, the ropes of gold chains (the *sautoirs*), to cameos and medallions, and carnelians were nearly as fashionable as they had been in Greek times. But such austerity did not last long, and soon precious stones were rimming the cameo and the dangling earrings shot fire and brilliance.

Sometimes fashion flickered from one shade of a stone to another. The fashionable sapphire for the first thousand years was a "sky-blue stone" and not the dark beauties we now admire. The apple-green shade of turquoise was the fashion during the fourteenth century in England. The rosy, almost pinkish spinel was the most admired, although it resembled the true ruby less than the darker ruby spinel.

The size of the stone employed also varied with fashion. From long before the time of Christ it was the fashion to wear huge stones—possibly of several hundred carats—as hat, helm, or hair ornament. Henri II of France stuck a fifty-four-carat diamond rather casually in his cap. Queen Elizabeth wore a great spinel the size of a baby's fist in her hair, and in the not so distant past Boston's own Mrs. Jack Gardner wore the Rajah Diamond and another of good size trembling in her pompadour.

While the stones of hat, helm, and hair were huge, the stones in rings were very small indeed. Possibly they had to be, for the fashion was to wear many on each hand and sometimes several on each finger. The Romans loaded their hands this way, and so did the ladies of the Renaissance. Whether the stones were real, let alone precious, one can't say, for a twelfth-century merchant might simply list his stock as "twelve gold rings with red stones" or blue or green. One has a better record of the Roman stones in fashion, for Pliny was on hand with his knowledge and comments, and Martial and Juvenal were there to poke fun at the fops—"six rings on each finger of Sardonyx, Emerald, Jasper and Diamond" (the diamond most likely rock crystal)—and Juvenal making nonsense by suggesting they wear light stones in the summer and heavy ones in the winter. Much earlier than that and in another country Aristophanes scoffed at the local dudes for wearing onyx rings "up to the fingernails." It is clear that the fashionable stones for the Roman matron were pearls and emeralds and the blue beryl, and as all kinds of quartz were arriving from India by that time the engraved jewel was enormously popular. Sapphires and emeralds were in plenty but were more difficult to engrave, and the beryls from India usually arrived pierced and strung on elephant hair and were thus unsuitable for rings, so the great stones for engraving were lapis lazuli, amethyst, jasper, agate, onyx, and the like.

Queen Alexandra wearing pearl ropes and her coronation crown, set with the Koh-i-nur and brilliants.

Color Plates

1. A collection of crystals including emerald, tourmaline, moonstone, aquamarine, kunzite, topaz, garnet, amethyst, zircon, and citrine.

2. Emeralds in the Crown of the Andes.

3. The beryl family: green, pink (called Morganite), golden, and blue (called aquamarine).

4. Section of a Chinese thumb ring in the form of a jadeite known as Imperial jade.

5. The highly individual tourmaline family, often showing many shades in one stone.

6. Sapphire (corundum family): pink, blue, green, orange, yellow, and white.

7. Large blue sapphire, believed to have belonged to Catherine the Great. (© *Life*.)

8. Star ruby (corundum family).

9. Group of cut and polished rubies.

10. Ruby crystal in its natural state, and a ruby, cut and polished, in a diamond setting. (© *Life*.)

11. An unusual pink diamond.

12. Brilliant-cut diamond of about fifteen carats.

13. Diamond ring of Queen Henrietta Maria of England, engraved with her arms and cipher.

14. Close-up of the brilliant-cut Regent diamond.

15. Alexandrite (chrysoberyl family).

16. Oriental cat's-eye (chrysoberyl family).

17. Cultured Japanese pearls.

18. Three cultured pearls: top, rose-tinted from Burma; lower left, cream-colored from Japan; lower right, white with a faint green aura from Australia.

19. Peridot (olivine family).

20. Black opal, which is usually predominantly dark gray, peacock, or sapphire blue. This wing-shaped example is from Australia.

21. The spinel family, many-colored, including three shades of red, one of them famous in the past as "the balas ruby."

22. Pink topaz—changed from its natural wine-yellow color through heat treatment.

23. The topaz family: wine-yellow, gold, and blue.

24. Garnets in varying shades: reds, greens, and orange golds.

25. Sphene, a little-known stone with more fire than the diamond.

26. Zircons—apricot-brown, honey-red, and golden-brown with blue (heat-treated) examples.

27. Amethyst, the proudest member of the quartz family.

28. An unusually large piece of perfect turquoise, embossed with gold on an antique hand mirror.

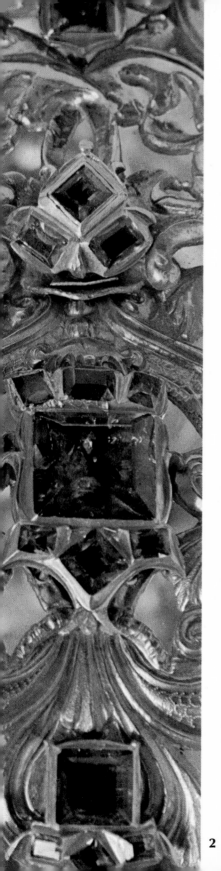

2

4

5

8

9

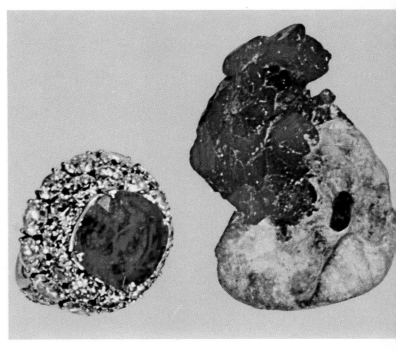

10

11

12

13

14

15

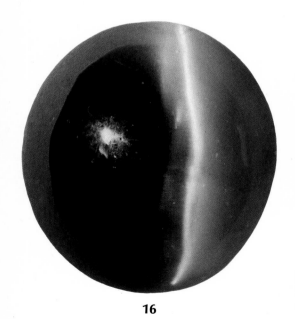

16

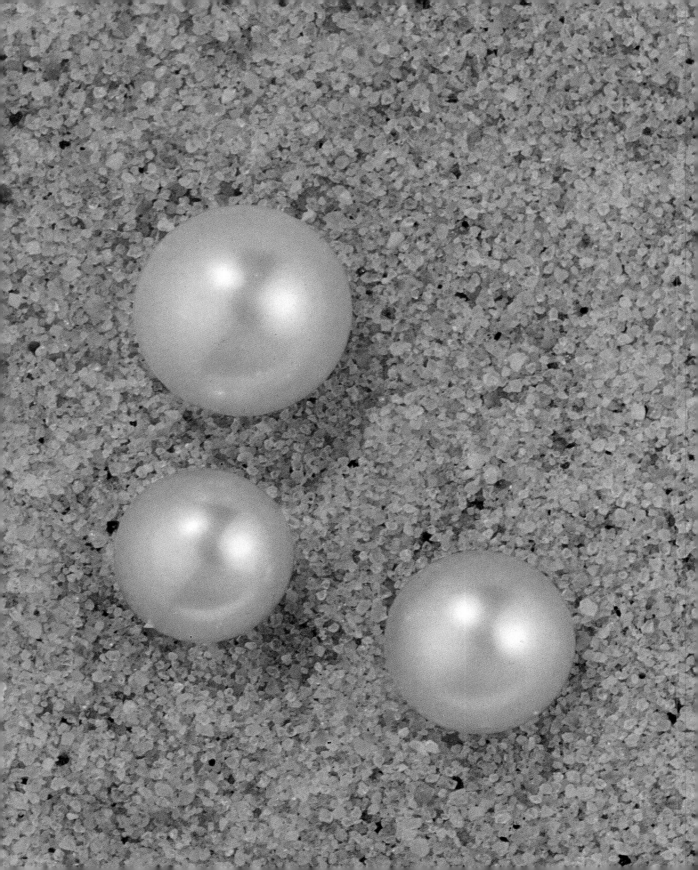

19

18

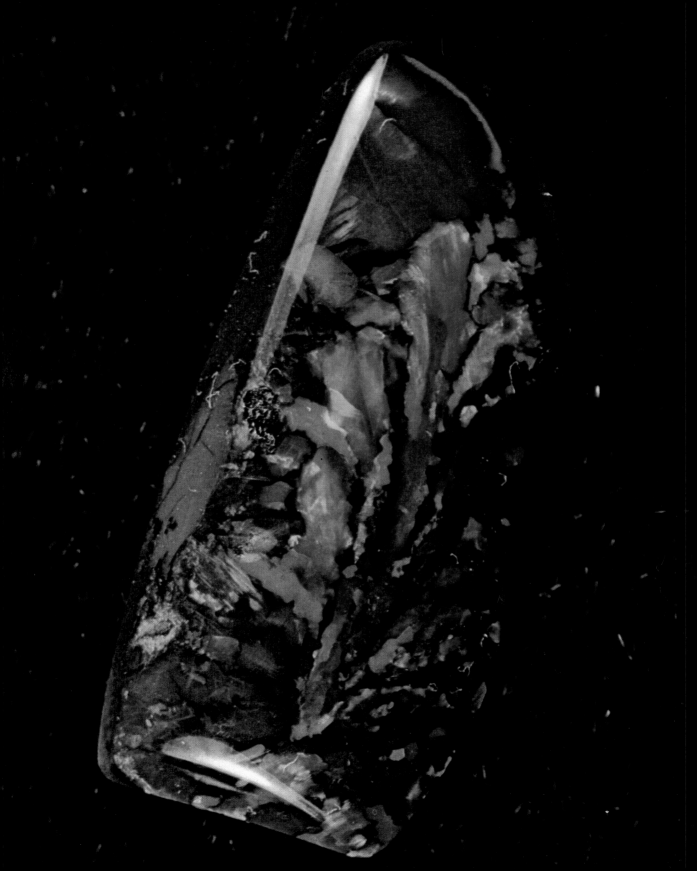

21

22

23

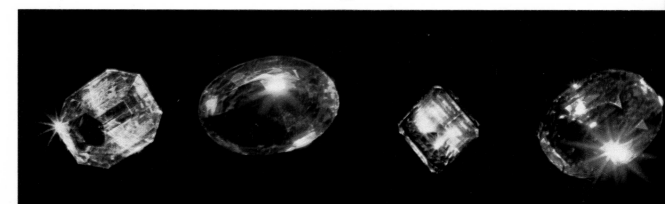

20

BIRTHSTONES MOST COMMONLY ATTRIBUTED TO
THE SIGNS OF THE ZODIAC

March 21–April 20: ARIES Diamond

April 21–May 21: TAURUS Emerald

May 22–June 21: GEMINI Pearl, Moonstone, Alexandrite

June 22–July 22: CANCER Ruby

July 23–August 23: LEO Peridot, Sardonyx

August 24–September 23: VIRGO Sapphire

September 24–October 23: LIBRA Opal, Tourmaline

October 24–November 22: SCORPIO Topaz, Citrine

November 23–December 21: SAGGITARIUS  Turquoise, Zircon

December 22–January 20: CAPRICORN Garnet

January 21–February 19: AQUARIUS Amethyst

February 20–March 20: PISCES Aquamarine, Bloodstone

Emerald, Aquamarine, and Related Beryls

Beryl: from the Greek *beryllos*—sea-green gem of the prismatic system. A hexagontal crystal with a hardness between 7½ and 8.

What to look for: transparency, clarity, and intensity of color.

Where found: Colombia, Brazil, the Urals, Tyrol, North Carolina, Egypt.

The beryl is a fabled stone. In ancient times it was called quite simply "the beryl" and defined by color: the yellow beryl, the pink beryl, orange beryl, etc. It was Pliny who first suggested that the famous and already well-known stone, the smaragd (emerald), was a member of the beryl family. Previously it had been considered to be in a family of its own. It was very perceptive of Pliny, for the smaragd is not even of the same hardness as the rest of the beryl family, and only in the early nineteenth century was it definitely established that Pliny was right.

Today most of the beryls are named separately: the emerald, the aquamarine, morganite, goshenite and only the golden beryl, yellow beryl, pink beryl, and orange beryl stay as they were.

Some beryl crystals grow to mammoth size and can weigh more than a ton, but at that size they are usually coarse and cloudy, and lack the transparency necessary to a gem stone. The greatest of the beryl family is, of course, the emerald.

Emerald: originally from a Persian word, reaching us through Greek, from Latin *smaragdus*. Thence to *esmaurde, esmaralde,* and in the sixteenth century to *emeralde.*

What to look for: color, transparency, purity.

The emerald is an extremely feminine stone. Since Ur of the Chaldees, the emerald and the color green have belonged to the planet now called Venus. One cannot help feeling that if stones had voices the ruby, in a rage, would shout, the sapphire growl, but the emerald would definitely scream.

The emerald had been known and respected since the Stone Age. Since well before 2500 B.C. it was mined in Upper Egypt, and it was there that the stone was first given a name. The Cleopatra Mines, located about fifteen miles north of Aswan, were lost for thousands of years, only to be rediscovered in 1818 by Cailliand on the orders of the then Viceroy of Egypt. One can imagine the romantic hysterics this must have caused around the world. Since then the mines have been opened and closed several times, but as the Egyptian emerald is apt to be pale and usually cloudy, it could not compete with the South American stones.

India had emeralds too—Rajputana has produced some first-class dark-green ones—but not in the profusion of Egypt. The emeralds referred to in old Indian manuscripts were more than likely green corundum or even demantoid garnet or peridot.

The emerald beryl grows in comparative abundance, but the fine ones rarely attain any great size. A twenty-carat emerald of fine color with a minimum of flaws is a *big* stone. Occasionally a freak of nature occurs. The Duke of Devonshire's enormous crystal, thoroughly flawed but of superb color, is two inches square and well over one thousand carats. It has never been cut, and unless it was cut into pieces, nothing could in fact be done with it. Ideally it would hang blazing from some throne or rest on a marble altar to Aphrodite; meanwhile, it has become a museum stone, a curiosity.

Emeralds grow in elegant, rather strict crystals, *soigné* and clean-lined. Because of their neatness and grace, in ancient times the stones were usually given only a slight polish, drilled lengthwise, and strung as oblong beads, something in conjunction with pearls. In the East, at about the time Darius sat on that rocky prow, they were some times simply set lengthwise and held at each end by golden claws or perhaps by a lion's jaw; or else they were strung and occasionally used as spherical terminals. Even as late as the eighteenth century in the Near East and Far East, stones were often simply polished and notched, so that they could be hung on a chain. The Indians and the Persians well understood the beauty of the suspended stone—a large gem hanging freely from a turban or throne with light playing on it from all sides. For all their lack of fire and brilliance, those great rough-polished stones, drenched with light and blazing with color through sheer size must have been wonderfully impressive.

Today the finest emeralds in the world come from Colombia and Rhodesia, although the Rhodesian stones never achieve the size of the Colombian ones. Both are of that green-of-all-greens, profound yet brilliant, that seems to be free of yellow, free of blue, a color that makes other greens look brown or ashen by comparison.

Brazil too has emeralds, usually of a somewhat lighter hue. Many people love them, as they are particularly bright and lively, with a high chiming note, and they are a *bit* less expensive, quality for quality.

At the time of the conquistadores Peru was thought to have emeralds, for the Inca treasure houses were full of them. Try as they would, however, even by the foulest means possible, the conquistadores could not persuade the Incas to tell them where the stones came from. The Incas swore there were no mines in Peru. Through all the torture and death the Incas were put to, they may indeed have been telling the truth. The stones very likely came from Colombia. In 1588 the Spaniards discovered the Colombian mines for themselves, and one wonders if they had any feeling of guilt at all—or was utter mercilessness the prime requisite of a conquistador?

At the time of the conquistadores the skilled lapidaries and merchants had no intention of risking their necks on the outward exploratory voyages. Consequently, the uneducated captains and traders used a rough and long outdated test for gems—hardness. The stone was put to the hammer. If it survived, it was a gem. If it shattered, it was cast away as valueless. Even the diamond can shatter, and a fragile emerald can fracture on the corner of a marble table. Bushels of emeralds must have been hammered into oblivion, casting a dancing green dust over half of South America.

Perhaps the greatest "collection" of emeralds in the world was housed in the Crown of the Andes, which is now in the United States. The history of the crown is interesting. Sebastián de Benalcázar, the son of a Spanish peasant, ran away from home to join Pizarro in the New World. He was a success, and Pizarro appointed him Governor of Quitos. On one of his forays he came to the territory of Popayán, an ancient Inca city high in the Andes, and there, in 1536, he made a permanent Spanish settlement. The settlement prospered, and Pope Paul III made it a bishop's see, whereupon the orders arrived and started to build monasteries and convents. The King of Spain gave Popayán its own coat of arms, and gold and jewels poured into the churches rather than onto the throats and fingers of the nubile ladies, for it was at a time when religious fervor was high; the Mohammedan Arabs had just been driven out of Spain, and kings and captains were as devout as cardinals.

Then came the plague of 1590. Possibly it was smallpox, possibly it was some virulent form of influenza. It raged through the country, and, medicine being what it was in those days, the death rate was devastating. The Bishop of Popayán began a series of prayers to the Blessed Mother, and somehow, because of a miracle or because Popayán lay so high and isolated, the colony escaped. In a wholehearted expression of gratitude the great families of Popayán decided to create a crown for the saving Blessed Mother, "the crown to exceed in beauty, in grandeur, and in value the crown of any reigning monarch on earth, else it would not be a becoming gift to the Queen of Heaven."

They made it in 1593. The frame was carved from a solid piece of gold weighing one hundred pounds, and in it were set the captured treasures of the Incas. Four hundred and fifty-three emeralds were used, all of them from the treasure houses of the conquered host or from confiscated mines in other areas. The chief stone of the crown is a dark, glowing beauty of forty-five carats, which was taken from the person of the Inca himself, Atahualpa. Seventeen large pear-shaped emeralds hung from the crown, and in all the emeralds added up to one thousand five hundred carats. Expert lapidaries were brought from Spain to cut and polish the rough stones, and while undoubtedly a great deal of carat weight was lost, a sun's worth of brilliance was added. It took six years to complete the crown, and when it was finished in 1599 it was placed with great

The Crown of the Andes.

(*Left:*) Francisco Pizarro, who conquered Peru. (*Right:*) Atahualpa, the last ruling Inca, whom Pizarro put to death.

pomp and ceremony on the head of the statue in the cathedral, establishing a ritual to be followed every year on the eighth of December, from that time on.

The crown is as beautiful as ever, the gold glowing softly as pure gold does, the emeralds leaping forward like green lance tips, but there are dents. A treasure like the Crown of the Andes could not be kept secret. Pirates and buccaneers got word of it and it became a "prize." As a consequence, a guard of young men was formed—the Confraternity of the Immaculate Conception, which still exists today—and when intelligence reached them that the pirates were in the vicinity the crown was hastily hidden, buried, or carried into the jungle. This happened so often that the soft gold was dented, but never a stone fell out.

In the Western world the Crown of the Andes was such a fabled object that people began to think of it as a symbol, a kind of mythical jewel like the Grail or the Philosopher's Stone—an abstract rather than an actuality of gold and crystals. As one looked at it, noble and shining, what one perceived was the very fragrance of faith and belief that had poured over it for many devout years.

Large, beautifully colored, unflawed emeralds of over five or six carats are so rare as to be prohibitive. Therefore one should appreciate the beauty of small intense stones. Their ability to be heard across a crowded room is no trivial accomplishment. A small emerald, even when lavishly set with diamonds, will hold its own. An emerald and a bright sapphire will extol each other, the blue exaggerating the green and vice versa. And several emeralds set close together reflect each other as if green, like laughter, were contagious.

While flaws are almost inevitable, the object is to find a crystal which at least holds them to a minimum and which is evenly pigmented. Unlike the darker ruby, sapphire, or amethyst, the emerald does not allow the cutter to create the illusion of all-through color.

The brightly colored, far from perfect emerald is a much merrier character than its peers of other colors. A poor sapphire or a clouded ruby cannot laugh off its flaws as can a lively emerald, which is one reason the down-at-heels emerald is so endearing and a rather good buy for the not too exigent.

A not very good emerald can be soft and mellow, trailing clouds and inclusions dreamily in a kind of musing sky green. When a stone has excellent color, even though it is streaky and full of inclusions, it still gives the impression of being in a perpetual state of delight, and while it isn't up to the emerald cut or square cut or even the brilliant cut, it lends itself charmingly to a cabochon cut or to carving. Even such an emerald can look fat and important when it is imaginatively set: caged, for instance, in a diamond-dotted gold net, or deepened by a jostling crowd of small dazzling diamonds, or carved. At 7½ it is easily possible to engrave, and it is still being done today. Since time immemorial the so-called mossy stones have been used for signets or for seals, or carved to honor or placate a god. The result is a great singing dome of emerald for a quite reasonable price: its lack of clarity hidden by the design, its pale color augmented by depth.

While the big Colombian emerald is without peer, both Siberia and Rhodesia produce smaller ones of equivalent rank and quality. Their whole cry is color. If they have that, they have everything. Emeralds also have a quality of almost physically soothing the eye. Perhaps it was not sheer ostentation that led Nero, on a sunny day in the Arena, to view the battling gladiators through a flat emerald beryl.

Aquamarine: from the Latin meaning "sea water."
What to look for: depth and evenness of color, depth of stone, cut, and shape.

The light and lyrical-looking aquamarine appears more fragile than the emerald, but in actual fact it is a little harder. It was so named by the Romans, but it was known long before that as the blue beryl. It is found with other beryls, but grows to far larger crystals than the emerald. In fact, in 1910 a beautifully clear and transparent crystal was found that was nineteen inches long and sixteen inches in diameter, and even the most pallid and desiccated emerald doesn't grow as large as that.

What is most prized in an aquamarine is strong color, free from green. The aquamarine with a greenish tinge appears far more frequently than the true blue, which is probably why the Latins named it "sea water"—and they didn't mean the fine singing blue of the sunny Mediterranean either. The aquamarine, either the perfect blue stone or the one faintly tinged with green, has a sea quality as well as a sea color. When you see a good one, beautifully cut, intense, sparkling, and brilliant, you half expect to see the white crest of a wave form somewhere in it and start to break in·the quivering blue. Even when it is square- or emerald-cut, it gives one the feeling that just around the corner of the stone is a golden beach or a green, sunny shore line.

By today's standards the fineness of the aquamarine depends on its blueness. It can vary from a deep icy blue, not unlike some Ceylon sapphires, to a lighter, chilled, but still greenless blue. Its color is not penetrating, and isn't meant to be. It has the light touch of a pink diamond or a yellow sapphire. You feel that it will have many flirtations in life but never achieve an Isolde or Juliet love affair.

A good aquamarine, sparkling and limpid, is well worth setting in diamonds, or, as it was during the twenties and thirties, with small rubies and diamonds in gold. It is lovely, too, heaped together with other pastel stones of equivalent intensity: a light lively amethyst, a pink or bright-green tourmaline, or with its sister, the pink morganite.

As the aquamarine can have brilliance, it is a pity to cut it cabochon. The only reason would be in the case of a stone of good color but inferior transparency. Happily, barring small accessory stones, this is rare. The aquamarine is at its best emerald-cut, square-cut, or step-cut if it is on both the front and back of the stone. The more light and play an aquamarine has, the better. For small fine stones the brilliant cut is full of life, and this is ideal when it is to be set in a necklace or bracelet surrounded with the fire of diamonds.

Morganite: named for the great collector J. P. Morgan.

What to look for: transparency, and either true nursery pink or tea-rose pink, depth of stone, good cut.

This is probably the pink beryl one reads about in medieval romances. As it was not really "cut" in those days, only polished, it could show no brilliance and made its name on sheer color. Today, along with pink diamonds, sapphires, tourmalines, kunzite, topaz, it plays a happy part in the fashion for pink stones. While the kunzite has an orchid cast and tourmalines run to rose, the morganite is delicately, definitely pink. It is found in two shades—true baby pink and pink tending toward coral, as in the California crystals. The stone shows those various twilight pinks that you sometimes get in a vivid sunset. Madagascar produces very individual colors; their morganite is a true rose red, their aquamarines close to some Ceylon sapphires.

When the stone is deep enough, the brilliant or step cut is ideal for the morganite, and it is well worth a platinum and diamond setting. Gold is sometimes too strong for the delicate tint. When played with other stones, morganite responds best to those of a blue cast—whether green or violet or blue. There is no excuse for a flawed or cloudy stone, as morganite grows in large, clear crystals.

Golden beryl:

What to look for: as pure a yellow as possible; if on the golden side, free from orange and brown tones.

Like all the yellow stones, the golden beryl is for the subtle, for those who can make decorating drama out of muted tones, who say riveting things in soft voices. It can sparkle with the best and, properly cut, shows considerable brilliance. Like all beryls (except the emerald) it grows in large, clear crystals. It has enough bite to its color to take gold as a setting, but seems to acquire added vitality set with diamonds. While it is sometimes called helidore, that is a name which should be reserved exclusively for the South-West African variety.

There are beryls of other shades too: the rare and beautiful orange beryl, a shade of yellowish-green, and, of course, the colorless goshenite (which was once found in Goshen, Massachusetts). But, barring the orange variety, they are seldom cut as gems.

Then there is the green beryl, which one may either consider as the poor relation of the emerald or, better, think of on its own. At its best it can be a lovely, lyrical light-green crystal, suggesting a teaspoon of Chartreuse dissolved in sparkling water. Brilliant- or step-cut, it is one of the beguiling pastels. Pure green beryls with enough color to have character are rare, however, and pale green beryls are washouts.

Chrysoberyl, Alexandrite, and Oriental Cat's-Eye

XI

C hrysoberyl: from the Greek, "golden beryl." Orthorhombic crystal with a hardness of 8½.
Where found: Brazil, Ceylon, China, the Urals.

The Greeks knew the beryl as a species, and, as the chrysoberyl they spoke of bore a resemblance to the yellow beryl, they understandably put it under the beryl heading. But chrysoberyl is not beryl. It is of a quite different structure and hardness. Nevertheless, beryl is what this species has loosely been called through the ages, until subheadings for the different varieties took precedence: alexandrite, Oriental cat's-eye, and what was sometimes called chrysolite. The name chrysolite was used in reference to other stones—yellow olivine, for one—which is another example of the ancients' habit of grouping stones of the same color under one heading. This simple form of chrysoberyl should be called exactly that—chrysoberyl.

Related to the spinel by chemical formula, kin to olivine in structure, chrysoberyl has its own distinct blood lines. To confound early mineralogists further, the three varieties bear no family resemblances. Barring the chrysoberyl, which is uncomplicatedly beautiful, the other two forms can be said to have a magical quality—so much so that if alexandrite had been discovered some hundreds of years earlier, it would undoubtedly have been the great talisman stone of all time.

Alexandrite, at its most perfect, is a clear, bluish emerald-green by day, but when the lights go on at night, it turns a warm columbine-red with hints of orange. If it is placed under a "daylight" fluorescent lamp it will, in a flash, turn back to green. The alexandrite is always cut to let the light play and refract to the greatest possible extent. The stone was discovered in Russia in the nineteenth century, on the birthday of Alexander II, the first Tsar to attempt real reforms. As green and red were also the Russian national colors, alexandrite became intensely popular, except perhaps with the Poles, who knew Alexander's roweled heel, and with that terrorist group known as the People's Will, who eventually assassinated him in 1881. At one time the alexandrite came only from the Urals, which made its scarcity value high, and even today it is from there that the best color comes. Later alexandrite was discovered in Ceylon and Tasmania

Alexander II of Russia, for whom Alexandrite was named. The stone was thought to have been discovered on his birthday in 1818.

—still showing its night-and-day magic. But while the stones from these regions are apt to be clearer, the green is darker, more a bottle-green or yellow-green, and the red is less marked than in the Russian variety. Catherine II of Russia was probably the most luxurious queen the West has ever known—indeed, it was she who made the walls of a ballroom at Tsarskoe-Selo entirely of lapis lazuli—yet for all her international expenditures Catherine backed the Russian mines with enthusiasm and developed a fine collection of "local" stones. She is often said to have had magnificent alexandrites, but this was impossible as they were not discovered until the nineteenth century.

Alexandrite, which is the most precious member of this family, is hard to come by. It is not coming out of Russia, and not much of it is produced in Ceylon or Tasmania. Perhaps if the world knew the stone better there would be a greater demand for it, but as gems go it was born only yesterday, and therefore has not had sufficient time to make itself known. Large as Russia is, alexandrite was a rather local fashion there for a short era. Its day will undoubtedly come, for, apart from its beauty, alexandrite is a very hard stone, ranking between corundum and precious topaz. Added virtues are that it is unlikely to develop flaws and it takes a brilliant polish.

Chrysoberyl cat's-eye, called Oriental cat's-eye or, in former days, cymophane (to separate it from other stones which show chatoyancy, such as quartz or tourmaline or a specially cut sapphire) had a long history. As the stone does not need or want a brilliant cut, its feline look was discovered early. It was necessary only to polish the pebble to show the line of light, and, as cabochon was the first attempt at cutting, it showed up right away. Cymophane comes from the Greek words meaning "wave" and "to appear," which describe it well. The line of light is best seen under direct light— either the sun or a lamp—and is more vague and diffused in general house lighting. A fine cat's-eye duplicates the yellow or green eyes that cats have. Smooth as glass and at a good hard 8½, it takes a fine and shining polish. The favorite color is a yellow-gold-beige (rather like whipped honey), the line of light being paler, yet clear and distinct. The intensity of the line comes and goes, which makes the stone look so astonishingly alive that some people are uneasy in its presence and find it disconcerting to catch the supercilious eye of an inanimate object.

A huge and glorious cat's-eye, better than three hundred and thirteen carats, was "presented" to Queen Victoria. It cannot exactly be called loot, but, on the other hand, the King of Kandy, to whom it belonged, was conquered, and almost without knowing it found himself giving it to the Great White Queen.

Naturally cat's-eye in all its forms has always been associated with the evil eye, just as cats themselves were. In the Far East it was believed that nothing downs a lesser devil so effectively as a larger devil. Three hundred and thirteen carats is large, so there are some who might be superstitious enough to say that this cat's-eye may have been protecting the British Empire for years—working its magic from some deep and dark London vault!

While quartz chatoyant stones are available, Oriental cat's-eyes are extremely rare and are snapped up whenever they are found. People in the Far East rank the chrysoberyl cat's-eye very high and seem to have a knack for knowing where to lay hands on these stones—and for closing their fists over them when they do. Not many arrive in Europe or the United States.

Chrysoberyl itself is a clear and lovely stone that varies in color from pale green-yellow to greenish-brown. The green-yellow is the favorite. What is valued in this variety is clarity and pristine color, whether this tends to the yellow or green side. Actually, it can have a very slight trick of its own, for a delicate play of color is possible but, unlike alexandrite, the play lies within the colors themselves and is a matter of shades. It does not achieve the opalescence of the cat's-eye, so it is rarely cabochon-cut, rather almost always step-cut or brilliant-cut. There is a handsome example of chrysoberyl in the Mineral Gallery of the British Museum: forty-five carats, clear, well cut, and of a bright transparent yellowed-green like a sandy-bottomed pool of clear water when the light slants through the grass.

XII

Ruby, Sapphire, and Other Corundums

C orundum: from the Sanskrit *kuruvinda*. Trigonal system of crystals with a hardness of 9.

What to look for: transparency, purity, color.

Where found: Burma, India, Ceylon, Thailand, the Urals, Montana, North Carolina, Australia, and Africa.

Corundum produces two of the king's ransom stones: the sapphire and the ruby. Those two lordly stones so dominate the picture that the other beautiful gem corundum is often overlooked. Because of its redoubtable hardness, when it is not of gem quality corundum is used commercially as the abrasive known as emery and often polishes its sisters and brothers. The proudest of the corundum family is the ruby.

Ruby: from the Latin *rubeus*, "red."

What to look for: transparency, clarity and strength of color, the clear, bright, dark crimson called pigeon blood.

Rubies are high-bred crystals. A first-class "pigeon-blood" ruby of any size—say five carats or over—is so rare that it is almost prohibitively expensive. The old cliché "rare as fine rubies" is no floundering generality but a hard fact. The reason is scarcity. The fine ruby crystal just does not form in large crystals. Some of the great jewelers will grow quite moist-eyed over the recollection of a perfect four-carat ruby they may once have held, whereas an eight-carat diamond of the same fine quality has to be recalled by reference to their ledgers. Because of its scarcity, the large ruby is, carat for carat, more expensive than a diamond of the equivalent caliber.

Even in the sixteenth century Tavernier was complaining at length about the small size of good rubies. Perhaps he had hoped to find some great specimens in India, and he went to much trouble in his attempts to find them. "After sixty days," he wrote, "in flat barks from Ava to Siren, with the woods full of lions, tigers and elephants, I came to the mines, but the stones were not large and I rarely met fine ones of more than three or four carats." He may have been a little shaky on natural history, or else some whimsical maharaja dropped a lion there just to astonish him, but his judgment on rubies was without fault.

There are those who genuinely do not care for rubies. When they hold even the most pure and pulsing pigeon-blood ruby in their hands—nothing seems to happen. On the other hand, there are those who feel so strongly about the stone that they would gladly slit a throat for one. The ruby seems to be a compulsive stone. Europe appreciates the ruby more than the United States does, and the Far East appreciates it so very much that it is difficult to pry one out of the East at any price.

The ruby, called by the Indians "Lord of the Stones," has many faces and creates many impressions at the same time. While the aquamarine seems to dance, its feet barely touching the ground, and the moonstone seems to hum in a happy preoccupied way over some amiable daydream, the ruby is both stately and passionate. One thinks of grandeur—of something from Macaulay's *Lays of Ancient Rome*:

> But hark! the cry is Astur:
> And lo! the ranks divide;
> And the great Lord of Luna
> Comes with his stately stride.

And one may also think of cruelty and roses, of slaughter and spices. Of all stones, the emotional range of the ruby is the greatest.

The ruby and the sapphire are identical twins. The only difference is that the ruby is given its color by a trace of chromium and the sapphire is pigmented by iron and titanium. The emerald and the aquamarine beryl are in a comparable situation. In both cases, too, one crystal, while following exactly the direction and habit of growth, grows larger than the other and in greater profusion. The sapphire can achieve a far larger crystal than can the ruby, and the aquamarine can outdistance its twin, the emerald, by hundreds of carats—which somewhat accounts for the difference in price.

The finest rubies in the world come from Upper Burma (although Marco Polo gave the laurel to those from Thailand). In Burma the splendid pigeon-blood ruby is found appropriately surrounded by a court of spinels, zircons, tourmalines, chrysoberyls, topazes, peridots, and all the other corundum crystals. In Thailand the rubies are slightly ruddier and have a smaller court, chiefly spinels in attendance, but—as if to make up for diminished numbers—among the other corundum crystals are found some of the finest sapphires in the world.

One thinks of the glowing ruby as being quite simply a cut and polished corundum crystal. The truth is that many crystals are that coveted deep red only in certain areas or, indeed, in streaks. Often the chromium trace which pigments it failed to

The finest rubies in the world come from mines like these in upper Burma.

permeate the whole crystal, or else another element entered or added its color. The result is a crystal as watery or as multicolored as a piece of Tiffany glass. Such a stone achieves its strength of color by cut alone.

The Indians were the first to master the art of cutting for color—that is, of cutting a stone that was patchily or unevenly colored. By using depth, light, facets, and angles they increased the spread of the color until, to the naked eye, all of the stone looked a heavenly crimson.

The Indian view—and they have been thinking and working this way for thousands of years—is that color is the chief beauty of a colored stone. The discovery of a form of cutting that gave more brilliance did not interest the Indian cutter. Such a cut took weight from the stone. He preferred the unbroken egg to the omelet. As a consequence, no one cuts for color like the Indian. He learned his trade well and was wise to be cautious, for there was a time when, if his cutting was poor, if he reduced the stone too much, if he failed to augment the color, he would have lost his fortune, and probably his life as well. The Code of Manu, written two thousand years ago in India, gives a very close description of the jewelers' craft and includes as an important part of the code the fines and penalties for bad workmanship or debasing gold. It was a perilous trade even in Europe, for the cutter was held responsible for the stone, no matter how recalcitrant and unpredictable it might be.

The Indians have always cut to keep weight as well as color. As the ancient Moguls considered stones a major part of their capital, paring the stone to get fire or brilliance would be like a man's nibbling away at his IBM stock to arrive at even numbers. What was the point? By and large the Moguls didn't *wear* their stones. They were for show, but primarily they were money. As it happens, in the case of the ruby and the sapphire the Indian cutters achieved both objectives, for depth is one way of achieving color.

Depth of color can be helpful to the ruby in another way as well. It is odd that no one mentions it, but the ruby is usually as thoroughly flawed as the emerald (its flaws are often of quite another order: "silk," though they can also have inclusions) but because of the ruby's color these "skeins" show less.

India has always loved the ruby since the days when all stones "red as coral and yellow as saffron" were reserved for royalty. They also applied the caste system to rubies, sapphires, and diamonds, and to the two former they gave a sex. Oddly enough, the Brahman in the case of sapphires was the light sapphire, and the lower castes and the female sex got today's coveted darker sapphire. The fine red ruby was Brahman and male. The next three castes were actually spinels and not rubies at all, but the Indians were not aware of that then. As a matter of fact, sex in stones (and often taste and temperature) was still an accepted thing in Europe until well into the seventeenth century.

Almost without exception, every *large* historical ruby that still survives is not a ruby but a spinel, and one must assume that the huge rubies mentioned in certain ancient manuscripts, tablets, or stones were in fact either garnets or one of the spinels.

Up until the time of Tavernier, all corundum in India was called ruby. There were red rubies, blue rubies, violet, green, colorless, and yellow rubies. Whether the Indians chose to call them ruby or corundum, at least they grouped them all, very rightly, under one family.

Sapphire: possibly from the island Sapphirine in the Arabian Sea. Blue corundum crystal with a hardness of 9.

What to look for: the velvety cornflower blue or the bright-navy satiny color or a dark electric blue; in lighter colors, vitality and good cut.

Where found: Burma, Kashmir, Ceylon, Afghanistan, Hindustan, China, the Ural Mountains, Queensland, Montana, Tanzania.

In his *Anatomy of Melancholy* Burton wrote of the sapphire: "It is the fairest of all precious stones of the sky color . . . frees the mind, mends manners." Really it is a very great pity that men had to give up jewelry, for they seem to have such a strong appreciation of, and affinity for, stones. The sapphire in particular seems to be a masculine favorite and is, apparently, the first stone a man thinks of after the diamond.

Sapphires, like the ruby and all other corundum crystals, are found in rock or in the beds of streams and they have been mined or panned for many, many centuries. In contrast to the ruby, the sapphire is found in far greater profusion, size, and variety of colors. Just as there was a time when all gem corundum was called "ruby" no matter what its color, today, barring the ruby, all corundum is called "sapphire": white sapphire, yellow sapphire, pink, violet, green, and gold sapphires, and an amazing orange sapphire which is properly called "padparadcha" and gives the improbable impression of a blazing, ice-cold bonfire. Then there is the strange sapphire that, it would seem, refused to make up its mind: the alexandrite-sapphire or the phenomenal sapphire. It is purple-red by day but, as artificial light kills the blue in it, it turns reddish at night. Of all these the blue sapphire is the most beloved.

The finest sapphires today come from Upper Burma, and the best ones are often described as Kashmir blue. Not to make the name totally without foundation, sapphires also come from Kashmir (perhaps they were found there first), but not in such abundance as in Burma. Kashmir blue is unmistakable. The color is cornflower. No matter how dazzling, it appears both soft and inviting. Of course it is anything but soft. Like all gem corundum, it ranks next to the diamond in hardness. Another great attribute of Kashmir blue is that it stands up to electric light beautifully. Where a less fine dark sapphire will turn navy blue and is at its best only in a strong direct light, or daylight, the Kashmir is always radiant.

Burma has its own blue which is no whit less fine than the Kashmir shade, but usually the blue is harder, sharper, and more imperious. The color is more electric than cornflower and so fractionally deeper and darker. The Thailand sapphires are equally fine, with a gentle satiny look and a hint more cobalt in the blue. But it's a case of matching up angels, for all are celestial shades; it's just that the Kashmir is the rarest of the three.

Once you have passed those royal blues, you come upon a whole running scale of delicate, vigorous, lively, and clear blues, any of which might be your idea of the loveliest in the world. It is here perhaps that the great stones separate from the beautiful stones. The deep blue ones are exceedingly rare, expensive, and unarguably glorious. The lighter ones are beautiful, lively, gentle, and more "possible."

Ceylon produces every shade of blue sapphire, from a good dark lively blue to deep icy blue, to a dancing lighthearted Alice blue, to an elusive sparkling light-but-definite blue. There are not similes enough to cover the variety of blues in a sapphire —which makes the description "sapphire blue" rather ridiculous.

Pink sapphires are lively. They dart and quiver like hummingbirds. Given the proper cut, they have great sparkle. There is a passing thought of blue in some of the pinks, and others have a delicate salmon cast. The bane of the pink sapphire is that it competes directly with the pink diamond—which has brilliance and fire and is rare among rare stones—but it stands head and shoulders above most of the other pink gems. It is too seldom set as it should be, with diamonds, and this is unfortunate, for it has every attribute of a precious stone.

The orange sapphire is one of the brightest suns of the whole nether world. It is really orange, but an orange of great delicacy: there is nothing thick or hot or rind-like about it. Because of its liveliness, it is a stone that blazes out across a crowded room and should never be set with anything but diamonds. As it is scarce as well as beautiful, the orange sapphire should not be used in a "throwaway" manner with other stones but should be made as much of as possible.

The green, gold, and violet sapphires—those three which are so often and so wrongly called "Oriental" emerald, topaz, and amethyst—do not particularly resemble the stones they have been identified with. Whether the word "Oriental" was meant to add prestige, or whether it goes back to the old habit of harboring all stones of one color under one umbrella, no one knows, but it does all the stones a great disservice. The colored sapphires should be classified as exactly what they are: beautiful, bright, unique of color, and hard—sapphires.

The green sapphire isn't at all like the emerald, nor is it like the peridot or the green tourmaline. It is a rather dark green, close to the shade of a magnolia leaf, but because of its great hardness it takes a dazzling polish, which is always spectacular in a dark stone. It has a certain dignity and reserve and needs the best cut possible and a diamond setting to add vivacity.

Violet sapphire, when it is clear and well-cut, makes the average amethyst look lavender. It can be a fine high-stepping violet or a smoldering Gloxinia purple, not puce, not mauve, but bright and true. Neither shade has the quiet nobility of the amethyst or needs it. The violet sapphire has quite a different temperament, warm and engaging or mysterious and rich. Good specimens are scarce.

The golden sapphire, one must admit, does somewhat resemble the topaz, but not if one wants to be precise. The golden sapphire tends more to brass than the wine-bright topaz, but, as it is even harder, its high polish makes it look carbonated and fizzing with life.

Yellow sapphires have been used a great deal throughout history, and long ago they were undoubtedly considered to be yellow diamonds. If they are of good color and cut, lemon-yellow and alive with brilliance, there is no lovelier stone, barring the canary diamond, for those who are partial to yellow stones. Even for those who are not particularly drawn to yellow, this shade of sapphire has a coolness and gaiety that are extremely attractive. The trick is to get a good yellow, not too pale—otherwise it looks like a poor white sapphire or an off-color diamond—and not so strong that its clear lemon shade has veered to a hotter, thicker yellow.

White sapphire has neither color nor fire, and so might almost as well be glass. The stone has foolishly been put in competition with diamonds or used as a comparatively inexpensive substitute, and before the jewelers clubbed together in the name of honor and general education it was most certainly sold as a diamond. But it is a bland stone, and is put to shame by the colorless zircon, with its splendid fire.

Star sapphires and star rubies are in a class by themselves. They are the misty-eyed beauties of the family, and when they have intense color many people prefer them to the transparent stone. There is something elusive and evocative in the come-and-go of the luminous six-pointed star in its soft, deeply colored sky. Actually, the star stones are usually rutilated crystals, massed with hairlike needles called "silk," not quite up to the challenge of a brilliant- or step-cut, which demand clarity, transparency, and, ideally, evenness of color. When the rutilated needles (minute canals usually) are oriented, the light is condensed across the lines of interference and the result is a star. Sometimes the back of the stone is hollowed out, and in earlier times primitive jewelers often simply scratched a star on the back, which of course resulted in a fixed "design," rather than a moving, floating star. The thing to look for in any starred stone is strong, definite color, and a come-and-go quality in the star.

The Greeks knew the sapphire and so did the Romans, and almost every European regalia included it. Very early on it entered the ecclesiastical world. In fact, as early as the sixth century a papal bull ordered that every cardinal was to wear a sapphire ring, and further specified that it should be worn on the right or "blessing" hand. In the twelfth century it was considered so particularly appropriate that the Bishop of Rheims spoke with what seems almost undue enthusiasm about its beauty and nobility. Oddly enough, it was at that same time the favorite stone of necromancers, who claimed that it enabled them to hear voices and make predictions. It was also considered to be a stone capable of reducing sexual appetites, which may have accounted for the Bishop's enthusiasm.

The sapphire was always a great talisman stone. Charlemagne had one, and this can be seen today at Rheims. It is a curious object: two rather pale cabochon stones set back to back, with a bit of wood from the True Cross pressed between them. Edward I of England had a sapphire talisman too, but, as he knew a talisman was effective only if worn next to the skin, few people saw it as it supposedly worked away at its magic under his jerkin or robe.

The sapphire of the ancients: lapis lazuli

Lapis lazuli: from the Latin *lapis* (stone) and the Persian *l'azulus* (heaven). Cubic system with a hardness between 5 and 5½.

What to look for: a deep violet blue, as free of pyrites as possible.

Where found: Afghanistan, Russia, Chile.

One reads of the sapphire dating thousands of years before Christ, but it has now been made abundantly clear that the sapphire of the ancient world was really lapis lazuli. The sapphire of the Assyrians and the Egyptians, the sapphire of the High Priest's Breastplate, and the covering of the King of Tyre—all these were lapis lazuli, which was regarded as a rare and precious stone. And well it should be. It was used for seals and signets, for jewelry, inlay, and bibelot. It was also the ultramarine pigment used up until the Renaissance and beyond, accounting for the splendid and lasting blue in many illuminated manuscripts. Usually it is found with pyrites—golden veins that run lightly through it. With its violet-blue tone or even its azure blue tone, lapis lazuli is quite as lovely in its opaque way as any precious crystal.

Lapis lazuli has always been rare. Until comparatively recently there was only one source, the Badakhshan district in Afghanistan. The mines there have been worked for six thousand years and guarded more carefully than any diamond mine. They were, and still are, almost inaccessible. Among the dragons that guard the way are marshes and avalanches, gorges, ridges, cliffs, snow, high winds, and bitter cold. There are no roads, and today one must overcome still another dragon, which is the requirement of a visa for Afghanistan.

The Persians called the stone *l'azulus* (heaven), from which came the French *azure*. It was probably introduced to Europe by the returning armies of Alexander the Great, though the Egyptians and Babylonians knew it long before. In the records of loot brought back from early wars, lapis lazuli was always listed separately and very often higher than gold.

In the modern world, the Russians in particular have always loved lapis lazuli and used it perhaps more lavishly—or at least in larger slabs—than anyone else.

The ideal lapis lazuli is violet-blue or blue-violet, free of golden specks or the

(*Right:*) A bull's-head ornamented with lapis lazuli. Detail from a Sumerian harp, 3100 B.C. (*Below:*) Charlemagne's talisman.

white ones that are apt to be found in the Chilean deposits. The Russian deposits do contain the golden pyrites but produce various excellent tones of blue.

Ideally, lapis lazuli with a green tinge is less desirable from a collector's point of view, but as the blue is of such ringing loveliness it is hard not to forgive a few little excursions off the path of perfection.

97

XIII

Diamond

*D*iamond: from the Latin *adamas*, from the Greek for "unconquerable." Pure carbon of the cubic system with a hardness of 10.

What to look for: color, purity, flawlessness, good cut.

Where found: today, chiefly in Africa. Also Brazil, India, Russia, Borneo, Australia, and, curiously, in meteorites.

The diamond stands alone—the master of them all. No stone can touch it for hardness, brilliance, and fire, and only its own substance can cut and polish it. It is unique and continues to hold its secret, for to this day it is not known exactly how the diamond was formed; one can only guess at the extraordinary juxtaposition of natural events that must originally have brought it into being.

Since earliest times the diamond has been associated with the highest form of religious experience. In fact, in Sanskrit the word means "thunderbolt," which is another way of saying "instant illumination," and this makes sense of the statement "the Buddha had a throne carved from a single diamond."

The diamond has caused more bloodshed than any other stone, and ransomed more lives. It has been used both as a poison and a cure. Its brilliance seems self-generated. Lighter than light, it gives back better than it gets, creating color from no color. It blazes with its own secret, radiant, independent, and completely desirable.

For years the stone was the exclusive property of royalty. In fact, the russet-and-cream beauty Agnes Sorel, mistress of Charles VII of France, was the first European commoner to wear diamonds. This was in 1444. By the early sixteenth century the diamond had become the royal "betrothal" ring and, as the earth was mined for more it became the standard engagement ring. The stone is also "a girl's best friend"—loved by "light ladies," which proves, if nothing else, the permanence of its value.

You look at a well-cut well-born diamond—and what new is there to say about it? The similes were all used up long ago, and most of them were inadequate anyhow. The diamond is *not* like ice and it is not like crystal, and you cannot with a straight face call it white. It is best just to accept the fact that the diamond is a stone which came late to man, then simply took over. While the large ruby is far more scarce and the perfect emerald far more expensive, the sphene has more fire, through some irresistible persuasiveness the diamond became the lord and master of the crystal world.

It is hard not to be overimpressed with the diamond, by the awesome facts of carats and creation, weight, dispersion, and value, until the stone itself is hardly seen for its "image." Sometimes it is good to remember that the diamond is primarily a cheerful fellow, a hearty stone, and that it is the sheer gusto and generosity of the small "setting" diamonds that swings whatever stone it sets to a higher, brighter plane.

To get things into proper perspective, it should be realized that there are more diamonds under the earth and on it than any other precious stone. Five tons are mined every year, but most of the specimens brought to light are dreary looking—gray, brown, black, usually opaque—and suited only for the grinding world of commerce. Only a small percentage end up as jewels. Those that do have another pleasant attribute. Whatever they touch they make more interesting or more beautiful. Rest an emerald or a topaz on a piece of driftwood and the soft gray makes the emerald blaze and the topaz look like a small sun. Drop a diamond on driftwood and the *driftwood* looks more silver, finer grained, more subtle. To an old and yellowed hand the diamond gives character and suggests a "history." It embellishes and bestows.

Diamonds are mined from "pipes" in the earth, panned from deposits (which are apt to produce the biggest crystals), and, today, dredged from the ocean. These, of course, are not ocean-born, but crystals washed down by the rivers from higher deposits.

The diamond can be an extremely neat and orderly crystal: precise octahedron that the earliest jewelers simply polished. Sometimes it appears to have no definite shape at all. Sometimes it turns up as a shallow "flat," a lopped-off, flattened octahedron, or as a twinned crystal called a "macle."

Although the Dravidians of India had known the diamond since before the time of Christ, no stone of any size has been recorded before 1000 A.D. The diamond Pliny spoke of as "having a hardness which was wonderful and unnatural" was quite small and, as he said, "the property of kings and very rare." The diamonds spoken of at earlier dates—King Solomon's Ring, the Breastplate of the High Priest, and others— were almost certainly colorless topaz or beryl or rock crystal.

In the beginning India and Borneo had all the diamonds. Perhaps the most famous came from the so-called Golconda mines in Hyderabad (actually Golconda was a diamond center, not a mine), and in the sixteenth century Tavernier described the near-by workings in detail. From him one gleans that the working conditions of the sixty thousand laborers there were hardly humane. Between the discovery of the mines and the present day, Indian sources have supplied the world with most of its famous diamonds: the Koh-i-noor, the Regent, Orloff, Sancy, Shah, Nassak, Pigot, Eugenie, Hope, the Dresden Green, and the Florentine Yellow, to name a few.

As so often happens in the world of precious stones, when one source began to dwindle another was discovered. Early in the eighteenth century, when Indian production was beginning to slow up, the great diamond mines of Brazil were discovered by the Portuguese, and by the 1720s they were in full production. The stones were not as large as the Indian ones but large enough—and of fine quality. Portugal brought them back by the shipload, with the inevitable result that, by 1727, they flooded the market and the price of diamonds slumped. Not only the price of diamonds but their value as a security tumbled, and many a country and individual, used to pawning a stone in time of duress, found it hard to get the price he wanted. The Dutch merchants who were still dealing in Indian stones were beside themselves. And so a psychological war began. The Dutch stone dealers with their well-established markets started spreading rumors that the Brazilian diamonds, "if they *are* diamonds, my dear fellow," were inferior, doubtful, off-color; that the whole operation was fly-by-night; that the stones did not wear well, shattered readily, or shrank in the wash. No matter how outlandish and disprovable the argument, little is ever needed to frighten a man off investing in a big diamond. But the Portuguese had been in the tricky business of stones for centuries, and without even a change of expression they shipped their diamonds from Brazil to their Indian possession, Goa, and brought them back as Indian stones.

It is hard to conceive of the wealth that poured out of the Brazilian mines in such a comparatively short time. Even when the total output was pledged to obtain money for troops (when John VI raised 12,000,000 florins for his war with Spain and France), or taken over by Spain, or lost and destroyed in the great Lisbon earthquake of 1755, or sold in France, the royal regalia of Portugal was superb, and enough of it is still to be seen in the National Palace of Ajunda in Lisbon to give one an idea of what it must have been like in the eighteenth century.

Among the stones brought back from Brazil was the Braganza, a diamond reputed to weigh one thousand six hundred and eighty carats, which would make it the largest diamond in the world at that time. John VI never had it cut but sometimes wore it suspended from his neck by a chain. It must have looked like a water tumbler! After pridefully proclaiming it over all Europe for a number of years, Portugal suddenly became very modest about it, and finally ceased mentioning it at all. Rumors began to circulate that it was not a diamond, but a great colorless topaz—and as Brazil is the best source of topaz, this seems a likely possibility. On the other hand, another theory is that the Braganza is the mammoth one-thousand-seven-hundred-and-fifty-carat pale aquamarine which is always on display at the National Palace. That seems equally possible, as aquamarine beryls of enormous size also come from Brazil. At any rate, the Braganza Diamond is carefully guarded and no one can see it. The Matan Diamond (three hundred and ninety carats) , which was found in Borneo in 1787, isn't visible either—which leads some people to ask if it is rock crystal, perhaps, or colorless beryl.

Again, just as the Brazilian mines began to peter out in 1860, came the discovery

The Star of Africa, a diamond of 530 carats, was added to the scepter of Edward VII.

of diamonds in Africa, and as of now Africa seems to be a source that will never run dry. It answers for ninety-five per cent of the world's diamond output. The African pipes produce really big stones. In India and Brazil a stone of two hundred or more carats was rare and became famous at once. Africa's record of the Cullinan, three thousand one hundred and six carats, has never been equalled. This was the stone, incidentally, that the famous Mr. Joseph Asscher studied for months before deciding to cut it. On February 10, 1908, in the early afternoon, he set the stone under the cleaver and gave it a strong rap. Nothing happened to the stone, but the steel blade broke. He hit it again, at a later date, and when it fell apart precisely as planned Mr. Asscher fell to the floor in a dead faint.

Large stones and stones in large quantities repeatedly turn up in Africa. A stone of three thousand or more carats represents a real problem in terms of jewelry. What can one do with a piece of dazzle the size of a golf ball—toss it from hand to hand and watch its fiery play? Today's jewelry doesn't run to great tiaras, or eight-inch shoulder knots, or *mondes* for the tops of crowns—and few could afford to use a three-hundred-and-forty-eight-carat diamond, as did the Nizam of Hyderabad, they say, for a paperweight. As a result, many of the gigantic African diamonds have been cut to more practical size—and probably annually many a Mr. Asscher quails at the task. But these great stones exist and in one way or another have to be marketed. Alpheus F. Williams, in his *Genesis of the Diamond*,[1] includes a list of comparatively recent finds of over a hundred carats, with sixteen between four hundred and five hundred, and fourteen of over five hundred. It is hard to imagine a stone that size.

In West Africa in 1945 a stone weighing seven hundred and seventy carats, the third largest in the world, was found in the Sierra Leone field. Only the great Excelsior, at about nine hundred and ninety-five carats, stands between it and the Cullinan. No other continent produces diamonds this size. Arkansas went quite wild when a forty-carat stone was discovered, and the whole state of Virginia celebrated the find of the twenty-three-and-three-quarters-carat Dewey Diamond.

While all the other stones are glorious because of the color innate in them, the colorless diamond manufactures color from light. But it does this only if it is properly cut, which is why it is almost a criminal act to cut a good diamond badly.

Until a diamond is cut it is visually quite uninteresting. Often it is greasy-looking or looks like a frosted pebble or lump of crystal. As late as the thirteenth century the Persians, who had been appreciating, handling, and conquering stones for hundreds of years, placed the diamond after pearls, rubies, emeralds, and even the peridot!

To the Indians goes the credit for first discovering that this adamant stone could be polished with itself. It could even be faceted by turning it on a small wheel and

1. London: Ernest Benn, Ltd., 1932.

102

using diamond powder as an abrasive. Their reason for faceting the stone, however, was not to bring it fire or sparkle but to conceal flaws, and the result was not brilliant. In fact, Tavernier reports that the faceted Indian diamond was the mark of an inferior stone. When the Indians came across a pure and limpid stone they made no attempt to cut it, but they polished it so that its ocean of clarity was revealed. They also discovered that, as one face of a diamond crystal is fractionally softer than the others, it could be engraved.

One of these engraved diamonds is the historic Shah, now at the Hermitage in Leningrad. It is flat, oblong, polished but uncut and most exquisitely engraved. One can't help imagining that it would be pleasant to hold: smooth as glass and cold, with the small rough spot of curving script one's thumb would seek. The Russians got the Shah diamond when their Ambassador was murdered inadvertently (or advertently, who knows?) in Persia. Rather than start a war, the Persians sent a princely envoy with the most exquisite apologies—and the diamond. The so-called Shepherd Diamond was also engraved but not really cut. The Victorians decided that it was a waste of a beautiful diamond and turned it into a fiery faceted drop, but thereby erased the names of the great Akbar and Shah Jehan.

The art of diamond carving didn't belong solely to the Indians, however. In the Royal Collection of England is Queen Henrietta Maria's table-cut diamond ring, beautifully engraved with her arms and cipher. The diamond has little life and no fire, but the carving is a real tour de force.

The Indians invented the point cut, which was usually the diamond's own octahedron shape polished all over. The table cut was the same except that the top and bottom points were flattened to create a rough table and culet. These may have been— in fact, they *must* have been—the stones spoken of from the time of Pliny to the fifteenth century as "polished diamonds." While the Indian table cut was primitive in its lack of fire and brilliance, it involved the most interminable patience. All one can say of these cuts is that they are brighter than no cut at all.

By the early thirteenth century some of Euclid's works had been translated from Arabic into French, and these began to affect the study of optics. Aristotle too had been translated and absorbed. But it was Euclid who proved most useful to the diamond cutter, for diamond cutting is half unbearable tension (will it cleave as planned?) and half pure mathematics. During the fourteenth and fifteenth centuries some experimentation was done on cutting, but it was as if "knowing better is not doing better." The cutters were wise in theory but weak on procedure, and to aggravate matters, it took a cutter with an extremely lavish patron to release diamonds merely for the sake of experimentation. So it was that both the point cut and the rather joyless table cut continued well into the latter half of the sixteenth century. Undoubtedly, some of the all-over faceted stones of India found their way to Europe, and France and Italy produced a few "experiments," but fire and brilliance remained hidden.

Gem historians have fought over the question of whether it is Louis de Berquem, a fifteenth-century Belgian who first cut diamonds geometrically, or Vincenzo Peruzzi, the sixteenth-century Venetian who first cut the full fifty-eight facets, to whom credit should go for being the father of today's cut. De Berquem, whose statue stands in Antwerp, where he is considered practically a patron saint, is usually given preference, yet in 1945 an expert called Henri Polak all but said that De Berquem had never even existed! At any rate, the laurel goes to Peruzzi for first deliberately producing "fire" in the diamond. Since then there have been improvements only on Peruzzi's basic theme. He

Cardinal Mazarin. From an eighteenth-century engraving.

placed thirty-three facets on the crown (the top part of the stone) and twenty-five on the pavilion (the lowest part), separated by the girdle. The facets had charming names: table, star, bezel, templet, quoin, lozenge, cross, skew, and skill.

In the seventeenth century, but before Peruzzi, Cardinal Mazarin took a hand in diamond cutting and the rose cut came into being. This was a flat-bottom stone with no table at the crown which was faceted all over from a central point. The idea of the rose cut probably came from India via Venice, a more faceted version of the old point cut—but it was the Cardinal who sponsored it, and certainly it was far more brilliant.

104

Today's modern cut draws the culet down practically in a point, so there is no "hole" to see through when the stone is held to the light. The so-called Old Mine Diamonds had, instead of a narrow point, a flat and sometimes quite large culet. Today it is the fashion to have the culets of Old Mine Diamonds "drawn down," which causes fractional weight loss but adds enormously to the brilliance and often to the value. It is certainly worth producing this added brilliance and fire—especially if the stone is fine—and not expensive.

Of the great registered diamonds and other historic stones the majority today are listed as "whereabouts unknown," or "said to be in a private collection," or last heard of in the possession of such and such a Maharaja. Some·of them may belong to owners who don't particularly want to advertise the fact that they own Philip II's Mirror of Portugal or the Dresden Green or the long-lost Moon on the Mountain. Many of them have been recut. You may be wearing a slice of the sixty-three-carat Kollur Diamond that Tavernier brought back from India in 1635, or of the one-hundred-and-ninety-seven-carat Florentine, that great greenish-yellow diamond that belonged to the Medici family. It is known that the Florentine was cut up, but what happened to the bits is not known.

One historic diamond that may truly have vanished forever is the Pigot Diamond. A man called George Pigot was, in the mid-eighteenth century, Governor of Madras. He bought himself an Irish baronetcy, which was not too difficult in those days if one had the cash. Whether the title or undisciplined acquisitiveness went to his head, Pigot was in the habit of accepting what he called "gifts of a trifling nature" from the neighboring maharajas, which seemed to dissuade him from invading their provinces. At any rate, the big Pigot Diamond was just such a trifling gift. This predilection became known, however, and on his return to England the Baron was thrown into jail, and there he died, having willed the stone to his sister and brothers. In 1801 it was sold at lottery, and after that some say it was, for a short time, in the possession of Napoleon's mother, who was a shrewd woman, trusting more in stones than in her son's future. In any event, it wound up in the hands of Ali Pasha, the Lion of Janina, who acted as the semi-independent despot of Albania, and whose curious court is so sensuously described in *Childe Harold*.

When he lay dying he requested a moment to make his peace with his God. It was granted, and he called to his side a trusted friend—a French soldier of fortune—and his Christian wife Vasilkee. Ali Pasha put the Pigot Diamond in the soldier's hand and ordered him to destroy the stone *and* his wife. The soldier claimed that he smashed the diamond to dust with a hammer. Possibly he did. However, Vasilkee, whom he certainly did not destroy, lived out the rest of her life in comparative luxury, possibly on the proceeds of its sale.

One other diamond that did withstand the hammer of steel and oblivion is the Sancy diamond, now in the possession of the Astors of Cliveden. Its story follows.

XIV

Saturday's Child: the Sancy Diamond

$\mathcal{J}$t is a story that will not wholly tell itself. Romantics took it up and tangled the skeins, but by letting known facts edit the fiction and allowing only a few not-quite-provables to tinge the tale, the story of the Sancy diamond might go something like this: One man gave his life to keep it hidden. Thousands lay in their blood because of it, and because of it thousands lived. Alone it swung a war, and because of it Henry of Navarre became King of France. It traveled, always on business, here and there: changing itself into carbines, cavalry, or just plain cash. It rarely played the jewel for long. Most of its life it worked hard for its living, which perhaps suited this bright diamond well. . . . Better to fight beside strong men and mold a country's destiny than to sit in a fop's cap, hang on a powdered bosom, or even top a crown.

The diamond first saw light in India long ago: heard the slave's cry, the trader's indrawn breath. It went to the cutter, who ground it on his little wheel, laying facets all around it, top and bottom after the Indian fashion. Then it went west in the soft darkness of a leather pouch tied to the neck of a merchant, and by caravan came to Constantinople and to Seigneur de Sancy, the French Ambassador there. It was in the year 1570 that De Sancy turned it in the light of a hard, bright, Turkish midday, recorded its carats—fifty-four in all—gave it his name, and straightway drew it into the turbulence of the War of the Three Henrys: Henry of Valois, Henry de Guise, and Henry of Navarre.

Patriot and loyalist to the bone, De Sancy loved his King—no matter which one —even the sickly, strange, and sallow Henry III, who reigned from 1574 to 1589—or thought he did, though all the world knew that while he played with lap dogs and minced, the dark voice of his mother, Catherine de' Medici, ordered France.

But Henry was his King, and so De Sancy lent his diamond to the kingly cap (for Henry always covered his head to hide an unnatural baldness), though sometimes, with apologies and tact, he borrowed it back again to pawn for the empty coffers of France.

106

Then Henry III was assassinated, and though with his dying breath he named Henry of Navarre as his successor, the throne went to the man who could take it. De Sancy at the time was colonel general of twelve thousand Swiss mercenaries "rented" by the Sancy Diamond. De Sancy opted for Henry of Navarre, who had a doughty fist, not a penny to his name, courage, and in spots integrity, and so he swung the Sancy-owned Swiss to the side of Navarre—and the rest is history: battles, the Mass in Paris, the start of a new France, De Sancy made Minister of Finance, and finally the Sancy Diamond redeemed from pawn.

It did not rest from its labors long, however. The story goes that it was soon sent out again to raise more money for Henry of Navarre. This time, De Sancy being busily occupied, as would be any finance minister of a bankrupt country, he sent the diamond out secretly with a trusted servant. Somehow, whether the news of this leaked out in the palace or there was a spy in the ministry itself, the mission was found out, and the servant had hardly begun his journey when he was set upon by thieves. Seeing the hopelessness of his situation, he quickly—and invisibly—swallowed the Sancy and, denying its existence to the end, was killed.

De Sancy was "immediately" informed, which in the sixteenth century might have meant an hour, a day, even a week. Knowing the caliber of his servant, De Sancy set out with all speed, and coming upon the body ordered it opened. There, in the stomach of the devoted man, glistened the Sancy, baptized now with blood.

King Henry of Navarre, now Henry IV, would have liked to buy the Sancy. If the tale is true, he owed it much and may have felt a deep or possibly superstitious attachment to it. Unfortunately, he could not buy it. The coffers of France were like a sieve, the crown jewels of Navarre were still in pawn to Queen Elizabeth, and he was not a man for frivolous follies, so De Sancy—who believed, like a true Eastern potentate, that a stone should work and not lie idle—sent the great diamond to his brother, who was Ambassador in London, and James I reached out his plump hand and bought it for 60,000 écus, the only major purchase of his reign.

For a short while the stone lay idle: half national resource and half toy. Then with James's son, Charles I, came troubles, including financial ones. In 1625 the King was obliged to pawn the Three Brethren, the great shoulder knot of Charles the Bold that Henry VIII had bought. It was, when Charles had it, comprised of three great balas rubies and a pointed diamond, which was supposedly the first one cut by De Berquem. He pawned it with other stones, but soon he was hard pressed for more money. In 1645 his queen, Henrietta Maria, bundled up what crown jewels she could, and taking all her own, fled to Holland to try her luck at pawning. Among others, she took the "second best ruby collar" of Henry VIII, the great table diamond called Mirror of Portugal (the stone Elizabeth I refused to return to Dom Antonio), and the Sancy. These she put in pawn with the Duke d'Eperon, and later, when she could not redeem them, the Duke released them to the acquisitive hands of Cardinal Mazarin, who had an eye that was impeccable, acute, and precise. Cardinal Mazarin, one may assume, loved diamonds more than God, for he left a larger collection of diamonds than of good deeds. Under his hand the Sancy lost its identity for a brief moment, as did the Mirror of Portugal, when they became part of the eighteen known as the Mazarin Diamonds. He left them all to King Louis XIV, some say out of guilt for all he had made away with under the mantle of the King's friendship. If Mazarin loved diamonds rather more than was seemly in a cardinal, the Sun King loved them openly and in his time managed to create the finest collection of crown jewels in the Western Hemisphere. He bought enormously from that fascinating traveler Tavernier, and among the more than a thousand stones he accumulated was a great one-hundred-and-twelve-carat violet-blue diamond known as the Tavernier Blue. He also bought other colored diamonds: pink ones in particular, yellows, and even a brown one.

If the Sancy was a vain stone, or a stone concerned with its place and rank at court, it might have had a bad moment when the Regent Diamond showed up: four hundred and ten carats of blazing white perfection, it could have made Sancy's not quite so perfect fifty-four carats feel a little inadequate, but one likes to think that the two took to each other instantly on grounds of sheer compatibility. They were both Saturday's Children. While they were the two chief stones of Louis XV's crown, and the Sancy sometimes hung like a giant raindrop on a jeweled spray and the Regent was later to adorn Napoleon's Sword of State, they both spent most of their lives in pawn buying protection, aggression, or defense for their country. Soon they were joined by another worker, the magnificent De Guise table diamond.

Off and on the Sancy was at court: dangling from an *agrafe* in a hat, hung as a pendant from a caracet, the necklace Queen Marie Leczinska loved so well: a velvet ribbon, studded with diamonds. And the Regent blazed among pearls as a shoulder knot for Louis XV.

Then came Louis XVI, a man so inert to the despairs and dangers of his time that on the day the Bastille fell his sole entry in his diary was "Nothing." Marie Antoinette was fond of the Sancy and was constantly having it reset: to sparkle in her powdered hair, to glisten like a dewdrop in a flower garland, to all but lose itself in a profusion of other diamonds.

Meanwhile the country began to move its shoulders angrily. Pleading and reasonableness had done no good, so sanity exploded into rage, but Louis XVI hardly noticed it. Even in 1790 when the Abbey of Saint Denis, which housed the tangible mystique of France, was pillaged; even when later they tore open the tombs to rip off the tatters of gold lace that still clung to the skeletons; even when the oriflamme, the golden banner of France which, according to the Song of Roland, Charlemagne received from Louis III in the year 800, was torn to shreds and utterly destroyed, still Louis was only confused and brushed aside the fact as if it was a fly he could not see.

On the night of September 17, in the year 1792, the Garde-Meuble, which

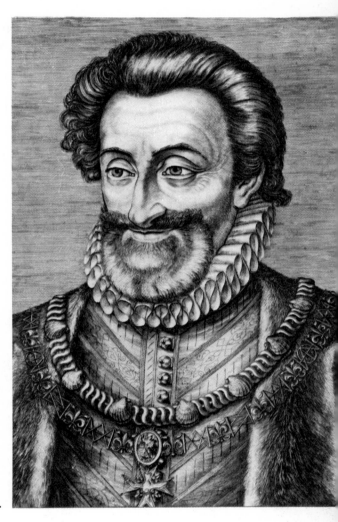

(*Above*:) Nicolas Harlai, Seigneur de Sancy.

(*Right*:) Henry IV, King of France.

housed the jewels of France in eleven cabinets, was entered—and emptied. It was a tour de force and makes small potatoes of *Topkapi* and *Rififi*. The great stones of France, the crowns, the orbs, the parures all vanished: the Sancy, the Regent, and De Guise, the Mirror of Portugal, and other Mazarins, the Tavernier blue-violet, the Côte de Bretagne, to name a few, a very few.

The truth about the burglary has never really been established. At the time every-

109

body was so busy accusing each other and defending his own innocence that any small voice of rationality was lost in the din. The real shock was to those who understood the import. The crown jewels were a major part of the country's capital. It might be rather like waking up one morning to discover Fort Knox denuded. But only the cooler heads realized the magnitude of the disaster. For the majority there were still all those "Aristos" to be beheaded, and jewels meant kings and queens, so who cared about them?

The Hope Diamond.

Marie Antoinette wore the Sancy diamond.

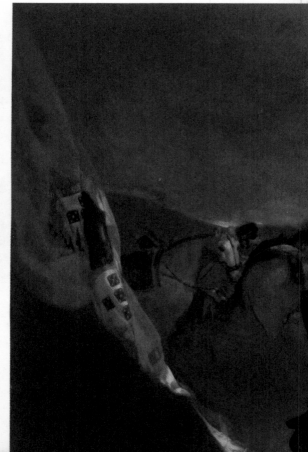

A copy of the crown of Louis XV which was set with the Sancy and the Regent diamonds.

(*Above:*) Queen Maria Louisa (by Goya), wearing the Hope Diamond.

(*Left:*) Manuel de Godoy, by Goya.

Mercifully, for the sake of the shaky new government as well as historians, everything was not lost completely and forever. The Regent Diamond turned up some time later, hidden in the timbers of a garret. It was reclaimed and put back to work—into pawn—immediately. The great Hortensia diamond appeared from the roof beam of a house in Les Halles. The Guise Diamond was found along with a few other pieces in the house of a certain M. Tavenal. Almost immediately after the robbery a rather suspect gentleman called M. Sergent, who had been in charge of the Garde-Meuble during the robbery, claimed that he had a bewitched magnet which, he believed, just might be able to find the jewels. Accompanied by some officials, credulous or cynical, who knows, and probably a good deal of posturing and clasping of the brow, he led them, blindfolded so they say, to the Avenue Montagne. There, dramatically, the magnet in his hand pointed to a specific tree. Men were ordered to dig at its base. And there, sure enough, was a substantial bundle of jewels.

Even with the recoveries, however, the loss was staggering. Gone forever was the Mirror of Portugal. The violet-blue Tavernier Diamond vanished and somewhere on its mysterious and unknown voyage presumably was cut into three pieces, only to be recognized many years later by Edward Streeter as what are today called the Hope Diamond and the Brunswick Blue and the one-carat bit he bought for himself.

And the worldly-wise oval Sancy? This vanished too. But then suddenly, from nowhere, it was in pawn to the Marquis of Iranda in Madrid, and so supplied Laselle's hussars at Rivoli in 1797 and Kellerman's cavalry at Marengo in 1800. The stone was not redeemed by France but fell into the hands of Godoy, Prince of Peace, who had made a kind of friendship with the French Revolutionary Government but was exiled in 1808 because of corruption in his government. He had been the lover of Queen Maria Louisa of Spain who owned the largest piece (now called the Hope Diamond) of the great blue-violet Tavernier, which had vanished with the Sancy at the Garde-Meuble. In fact, she was painted wearing it. Godoy died in Paris, having written sixteen volumes of memoirs in which he did not tell all, and the Sancy was bought by Prince Anatole Demidoff in 1828 and was carried off to Russia. It is easy to imagine Sancy there in the nineteenth century: barbaric luxury, outrageous empresses, and crazy courage, but little is known of its life in Russia or how it was used or set. It was in splendid company, however, with the great Orloff Diamond, the uncut Shah, the enormous red spinel that topped the Russian crown.

In 1865 Sancy changed masters again (for a hundred thousand dollars), and this time life was a little infra dig for a stone used to warriors, to hemispheric scheming and episodes of the most exquisite frivolity at the French court. It was sold to a Parsi from Bombay who understood its value but nothing of the life it was used to living.

And then in Paris, in 1906, Lord William Waldorf Astor bought it for his sharp-tongued fiery American daughter-in-law, Nancy Langhorn of Virginia, and set it in a great diamond tiara. In England Sancy once again played the role of jewel, and went

Lady Astor.

to court and the opening of Parliament and was at ease, as by that time it knew every in and out of ritual and pomp. Now it was no longer Saturday's Child. The Astors own it and may wear it when they please, though the occasions grow less and less frequent. It rests, indolent and beautiful, on its laurels. "Unless I am needed," says Sancy quietly. "Until I am needed."

Garnet

XV

A Frankish pin set with garnets. Seventh century.

*G*arnet: from the Latin *granatus* ("having seeds") and so related to pomegranate. A large, multicolored, loosely related family of minerals with a glossy to adamantine luster and a hardness of 6½ to 7½.

What to look for: liveliness or clarity of color; transparency.

Where found: different colors in different locales.

You might suddenly see a great pulsing red stone with purple and crimson stirring in its depths and shafts of scarlet darting at you as you move toward it, only to be told that this mysterious beauty is a garnet. Your face falls, and you can hardly see the stone for what you "know" about it.

But anyone who considers the garnet a lowly or inferior stone and associates it with dark Victorian brooches, class rings, or Aunt Maude's dreary bangle should look at the stone with new eyes. The darting and delightful green demantoid garnet is one of the rarest and most enchanting stones on earth. The clear orange hessonite all but flares right out of a setting. The red garnet was the "carbuncle" of the ancients, that much-rhymed stone that hung at the throats of the Egyptians, glowed on wrists, shoulders, and brows of ancient Greeks, and was cherished and respected by the Romans and countless latter-day heroes and heroines. It was treasured by the Anglo-Saxons and the Merovingian kings, and glittered or smoldered right on through the Middle Ages. It held a high place in the hierarchy in those days—and it responded.

The trouble with the garnet is that the green (demantoid) garnet is too scarce, and the red garnets aren't scarce enough. Red ones, in good crystals, are found everywhere from Ceylon to North Carolina and half the places in between—and they are not expensive. They are found in metamorphic limestone, in peridotite and serpentine,

114

in igneous rock, and in placer deposits. The hardness of the stone is respectable: it equals the beryl and is well ahead of the precious opal, but pure lavishness has sounded its death knell.

Most of us, having been brainwashed by the dark and depressing parures of the turn of the century, forget the many beautiful colors garnets can have. Badly cut, a garnet can indeed be a melancholy object, lugubriously red and usually in a brown study; but a clear and well-cut garnet can be as bright as a zinnia, as dark as a bottle of red ink, as green as an emerald or the very green of a dew-moistened leaf of the lily of the valley.

The chief divisions are: pyrope, almandite, rhodolite, and andradite.

Pyrope, from the Greek "fiery-eyed," is a warm, deep-red stone, at its best completely free of any tinge of yellow. Sometimes rose-cut, it was the pet of the nineteenth century.

Almandite (the name Pliny gave it) is almost certainly the "carbuncle" of the ancients. At its best it is the fine red of a bottle of claret in the shade, with bright sun behind it. Like some sapphires, it shows itself best in a strong light. Sometimes it has a royal cast of purple.

Rhodolite is, chemically speaking, a mixture of the two stones just described, and is often quite a lively rose-red and sometimes a rosy purple. It is both beautiful and rare.

In the group of garnets called andradites are some scarce and exciting stones:

Topazlite—a lovely clear stone, colored like either a Moselle or a sweet sherry.

Demantoid, sometimes called "Uralian emerald," is a fine transparent green, and very rare in anything over two or three carats. This is just as well for the emerald, because the demantoid has fire too. It is quite lively and high-pitched in tone, with an extraordinarily high dispersion—next to that of the diamond, in fact. Fire is most unusual in a colored stone and very exciting to watch, so the demantoid should *always* be brilliant-cut.

Perhaps the most unusual garnet is the blazing emerald-green uvarovite, which is found principally in the Ural Mountains, usually, alas, in such small crystals that it is unusable as a gem.

There are other garnet groups, but they are seldom used as jewels. Spessartite is very rare, transparent, and comes almost entirely in shades of brown or brownish-red and a vivid, sought-after orange.

Grossularite (from the Greek word for "gooseberry") comes, among other colors, in a jade green which is sometimes called Transvaal jade, and is an opaque stone. Mostly, the crystals are not transparent enough to cut, but the yellow and cinnamon ones often are. These are found under the name of hessonite or cinnamon stone. Sometimes they are called hyacinth or jacinth, which they most definitely are not—for these are both very old-fashioned descriptive names of the zircon.

XVI

Jade

Jade: from the Spanish *piedra de ijada*, meaning "colic stone." Crystalline aggregates with a hardness of: nephrite 6½; jadeite 7.

Where found: jadeite chiefly in Burma. Nephrite in China, Turkestan, Siberia, New Zealand, Canada, and the United States.

Jade, perhaps more than any other gem, can turn collectors into madmen. They develop an alarming must-have gleam in their eyes and a money's-no-object attitude that is almost frightening. They give the impression that there isn't much they wouldn't do to possess this or that particular piece.

It is easy enough to get lost in the romantic appeal of jade, even when one knows nothing about it. Effortlessly, it can summon up associations: visions of ancient Chinese courts, smiling Burmese temples, small statues of still, joyous Buddhas, of nearly transparent cups, translucent necklaces, and small, subtle fingering pieces, all of which establishes a kind of exquisite antiquity for jade.

Yet jade is far, far older and infinitely tougher than that. The Buddha died around 483 B.C., but the Swiss Lake Dwellers *stopped* using jade around 1500 B.C., and the Egyptians were using it between 4000 and 5000 B.C., although it was not used for ornament then. Both jadeite and nephrite (two quite different minerals lumped under the heading of jade) are tough aggregates of compressed fiber, and nephrite has a greater compressive strength than steel. Because of this sturdiness, both forms were used for axheads, knives, spear tips, and other instruments of war. In fact it wasn't until the beginning of the Chou Dynasty, about 1722 B.C., that jade began to be used for aesthetic purposes. Along with the diamond and corundum, jade is the only gem respected for both its utilitarian uses and its beauty.

The Chinese word for jade is *yu*, and the Japanese words are *giuku* and *tama*, all three of which signify both jade and precious stone. Our word came from the Spanish conquistadores, who saw the natives of Mexico using it as medicine, chiefly for kidney ailments.

Jadeite, which is a little harder than nephrite and infinitely rarer, is a pyroxene (which also houses the beautiful pink kunzite and green hiddenite). Some say it is also found in China and Tibet, but the great world source is Burma. For all its associations with antiquity in China, jadeite actually was not introduced into China until the eighteenth century. From that moment on the Chinese placed it above all other gems, gave it metaphysical attributes, and made it the symbol of the five cardinal virtues: charity, modesty, courage, justice, and wisdom.

Jadeite can be translucent or opaque. Its luster varies from a little less than glassy to pearly. It comes in an extraordinary range of colors: white, gray, orange, mauve, brown, black, and nearly every representation of green—from the most ephemeral predawn sky green to nearly black.

One shade of jadeite stands apart and alone, rare, precious, and revered wherever it is found—which is nowhere but in Burma. It is the shade often called Imperial jade, which has the pure green of an emerald, and as jade *aficionados* like to point out, an emerald without flaws, without fragility, with a calm high beauty and a texture that impels touch and that has the most penetrating green of any gem. This spectacular version was called Imperial jade because the last Empress of China (the one who was forced to flee during the 1912 Boxer Rebellion) valued this particular shade above all other jades or jewels, and saw to it that every fine specimen found was first shown to her. Even the ones she rejected still had the right to be called "Imperial." Her collection was incredible: three thousand ebony boxes full. And, as this exceedingly rare shade is not found in large portions, the number of pieces in those boxes must have been uncountable. The Empress always had with her a fingering piece of this jade, which served roughly the same purpose as Greek conversation beads: to maintain an inner tranquillity, or at least to encourage it. The theory is that if the body is given some small activity it will keep quiet and not twitch and itch and wriggle, for if the body is kept in complete stillness, unless one is a trained monk or lama, it grows restless and irritable and begins to demand notice.

Though one might hesitate to say it in the presence of an Imperial-jade fan, jadeite is also found in other rare and exquisite colors. There is a remote and silent mauve for instance, which is like lavender dissolved in milk. There is a gray as cool and unthreatening as the light storm clouds in a Chinese painting. There is an orange as warm and glowing as if it had trapped the sun in its fibers, and, of course, all the greens.

Jade is not sold or bought as other precious stones might be. A stone buyer can examine a corundum crystal or a beryl: hold it to the light, look through it, weigh it, test it in a hundred stringent, subtle, or standard ways. With jade, a man simply buys a boulder! Maybe it shows a rivulet of green on the surface but, *caveat emptor*, who knows what is inside? Possibly the layer is half an inch thick, possibly half a centimeter, or, as these men are dreamers and gamblers, possibly half a foot. They take a great chance, these buyers, for the price is enormous. One boulder sold quite recently for well over a hundred thousand dollars. The boulders are not broken up as other minerals might be; they are so tough they cannot be shattered with a hammer, and so until quite recently the ancient manner prevailed: the boulder was heated to a great temperature, then doused with cold water until it cracked. Today the diamond saw does the trick.

Nephrite, while it is a many-splendored thing, is fractionally softer (though no less tough) than jadeite, lacks some of the rare colors, and has a glistening, almost greasy luster once it has been worked and polished. Possibly the most precious form of nephrite is the so-called mutton-fat jade, which is especially coveted in the East; a cream white with an almost imperceptible breath of gray—or is it beige? Small matter, for it is hardly there, and only in the shadows of a carving.

Spinach jade describes itself precisely and is extremely popular, as it has a certain vigor of tint the other shades lack. Nephrite is found in gray too, sometimes the color of a thundercloud, and in yellow, as well as black. Like jadeite, all jade is apt to be mottled in color, which, while it causes some displeasure to the exigent, in no way detracts from its attractiveness. In some ways and in some colors, the uneven coloration adds a look of translucence, suggests something stirring softly in its quiet depths. Often the coloration will be various: a gentle green with swirls of mauve; or one called Moss in the Snow, which is white with fluent, swirling streamers of green.

Possibly it is jade's character as much as its beauty that gives it such a special place in the world of precious things: the impression of sturdiness, of unshakableness behind its soft, beautiful serenity.

A group of figures carved in jade.

Peridot

XVII

The peridot in a modern setting with turquoise and diamonds.

*P*eridot or olivine, from "olive." Crystals of the orthorhombic system with a hardness of 6½ to 7.

What to look for: clarity, velvetiness, strength of color.

Where found: originally Zeberged (an island in the Red Sea), Upper Burma, Arizona, Brazil.

Olivine has often been confused with emeralds, green sapphires, and even chrysoberyl, for its greens and yellows are various and range between the two colors in almost every shade and degree. In one aspect it *is* stable—it has been loved and cherished since time immemorial—and has been treated as a "harder" gem than it is. The form of olivine known to the jewelry world is the peridot, which runs the range of light yellow-green to a dark, almost brownish green. The mineral olivine itself is very common in nature, but gem-quality peridot crystals of any size worth considering are not. In fact, good crystals are rare, as the conditions necessary to form one are demanding and involve a complicated and infrequent arrangement of gases and liquids and temperatures, but when good crystals do occur they are incomparably lovely.

Peridot is used as a jewel, predominantly, in two shades. The lighter version, when flawless and well cut, looks like a glistening golden syrup lightly reflecting some mild, cool green sea. You are not fully aware of the green, it is just that the color is the exact opposite of brash and hot yellow. The second variety is the youngest and grassiest of all green crystals, which when well cut has great gaiety and a high, clear note. In fact, a handful of faceted green peridots sparkling together suggest a twittering of green birds. There is no blue in the green, even in its darkest version of itself. Place it in the shade and it still remains sun-touched. Oddly enough, for all its lively vivacity, it shares with the sapphire a quality of velvetiness—it glimmers and glows and draws you into the stone. The best peridot is the greenest one, and because of the hint of yellow, it loves electric light (it has been called "evening emerald") as well as daylight. It is a gentle stone, for all its dazzle, and its allure is feminine and subtle.

There are sapphire lovers, turquoise devotees—but peridot, like emerald-green jade, makes addicts. Once a woman starts with a peridot she keeps on going. They are among the most subtle of stones, and, whether they send out compelling rays or whether their gay spring green evokes all of nature to the eye—who knows?—but you'll rarely see a woman with only *one* peridot. Happily, rare as good ones are, their price has never been prohibitive.

Peridot in both its shades is an ancient and revered gem. It ranked in antiquity with emeralds, lapis luzuli, turquoise, and carbuncles. By 1500 B.C. the Red Sea deposits were already being worked. Zeberged, which is the Arabic word for olivine, was known as the Isle of the Serpents, which indeed it was. What is more, as the inhabitants of the island were the "workers" the kings did not like finding, annually, the dead opposite of a population explosion, so one Egyptian king ordered a whole campaign just to get rid of these deadly snakes, whose presence slowed up the mining operations enormously. The stones were so valued that life on Zeberged was tense: guards were posted all around the island to kill intruders on sight. Supply boats came sporadically, and there was famine—and so murder as well as death.

It is more than likely that the yellowest shade of peridot was the "topaz" of the ancients, as Pliny in his careful description places the "yellow-green" stones as having come approximately from Zeberged. Pliny did better than most, but there was a tendency to lump stones by color. In Pliny's day there was no Gemological Institute to appeal to, and one cannot help admiring him for the courage and modesty with which he made his statements and for the astonishing accuracy of so many of his judgments. Because of these confusions—which could only have been worse before Pliny's time— possibly yellowish peridot too is one of the Twelve Stones of Antiquity, and not the topaz at all. In any event, it is a highly romantic stone, with a long, dramatic history, and it belongs to the subtle and mysterious kind of woman who prefers quiet colors.

While peridot was well known to the ancients—particularly the yellow shade which they called the "gem of the sun"—the lovely green peridot was really introduced to Europe by the returning Crusaders. Once they got their account books straight, the thieving stewards hanged, and their wives' chastity belts off, they began distributing presents to the church, their beloved, their king or liege lord, and friends—rather in that order. What they *thought* they were giving were emeralds. Their Arabic was possibly a little shaky; stones had a way of switching and adopting names that must have made the contemporary lapidary uneasy. How could the average Crusader hope to know an emerald when he saw one? He did, however, know a beautiful thing—and the green peridot is certainly that. Some of these Crusader "emeralds" are still to be seen in the churches of Europe.

Burma knows the peridot too, from the same area as the great pigeon-blood rubies, and the Navajo Indians of Arizona have them in a lighter but good, true green.

XVIII

Opal

Opal: from the Sanskrit *upala*, meaning "precious stone." Amorphous, the opal is silica gel: hardness between 5½ and 6½.

What to look for: vitality of color, brilliance of play, good polish, no visible cracks, size, and depth.

Where found: today, mostly in Australia and Mexico; formerly in Hungary and India.

Even the most uninformed could guess that the opal is basically liquid, for it so closely resembles an oil slick in the sun. Its gambol of colors is due to the fact that it was formed of a series of solutions, sliding over each other at different times and drying out at different speeds. Light refracts on the inner fissures and layers, and the result is colors.

There are at least sixteen varieties of opal, but only a few come under the heading of precious opal. The rest are poor relations, although some are very attractive. Of the few opals used as gems, the most precious are the so-called black and white opals, which in fact are neither black nor white. The white opal, which has been known for several millennia, looks almost as if the liveliest pastel confetti had been dropped in a bowl of skimmed milk (or pale green or blue silk) and stirred slightly. It shows a dazzling but delicate play of red, blue, green, violet, and yellow, which, because the colors swirl in lightness, appear higher pitched than the colors in the black opal. The black opal was discovered only in 1905 and comes almost exclusively from the mines at Lightning Ridge on the border of New South Wales and Queensland in Australia. It is usually predominantly dark gray, peacock, or sapphire blue, with areas of emerald-green and flashes of red and yellow and violet.

The blue or peacock opal is either entirely blue or blue with purple or green, and the green opal is a play of nothing but greens, in a giddy whirl. The harlequin opal is less a matter of color than design. Here the colors are played against a reddish background in tidy areas, like a neat mosaic instead of the usual spontaneous now-you-see-it, now-you-don't. Hydrophane is a sad, cloudy, dehydrated white opal, which can occasionally, if dropped in water, show a nostalgic little play of color; and the hyalite opal is colorless and transparent and looks like molten glass: a changeling in this colorful family, but an opal none the less.

The fire opal is the only member of the family that can take a brilliant cut. It comes from Mexico, and it can be red or orange or yellow or, with luck, it will have a play of all three colors. A very exciting and evocative stone—just right for one's image of an ancient Aztec sun worshiper.

Barring the fire opal, the proper look for a precious opal is freshly oiled, as if only a transparent film held the frolic of colors in check. The hazards of the opal are scratching, as it is comparatively soft, and splintering, if it is dried out. As the opal is confected of semi-dried-out solutions (the amount of fluid in a precious opal varies from six to ten per cent), it can and may dry out further with the years. When opals are worn as rings or bracelets and thus subject to scratching and banging, they should go to the jeweler's every once in a while for a polish. They come up beautifully, glossy and alive once more. How often they should be polished is a matter of the wear, tear, and dryness. When an opal begins to lose its slick, sleek luster—that is the moment.

Some of the less precious, or "common," opals have a certain enchantment, if you forget about a play of color and just settle for lovely "still" color. The prase opal is a delicate young-leaf-green shade, the most thirst-quenching color imaginable, and the rose of quinzite opal is a nursery pink. The girasol opal has a blue-white sheen and sometimes a faint opalescence. Milk opals are found in various white shades: blue, yellow, or green, and of course white, a creamy, whole-milk color in this case.

Then there are the resin opal, found in bland beiges and mild yellow; agate opal, which is banded like the agate; and opal jasper, which might as well *be* jasper, as far as the eye can tell. Then there are opalized bones and shells; and finally wood opal, which is opalized wood, and there the play of color swirls with the grain—a strange and lovely thing, but a treasure for the library table rather than a jewel.

Originally India or thereabouts was the opal center (hence the Sanskrit word), but from Roman times it was probably Hungary, for the mines in that country are known to have been worked prior to 1400 A.D. European travelers reported on them at that date, but almost certainly these were the mines that served the Roman market a thousand years earlier. Just as the Hungarian mines began to peter out came the big strike in Australia, who has had the market ever since. What today one would call the Czechoslovakian mines cannot compare with either Australia's spectacular output or the unique fireworks of the black opal. Opals, of course, are found in other areas: Honduras, Nevada, Idaho, Brazil, but not in the profusion of Australia.

No stone has had such a baffling history as the precious opal. For many years the stone has been considered "unlucky." The truth of the matter is that the opal *has* been unlucky. From a stone once regarded as most precious (Pliny ranked it right next to the emerald) it became a fallen stone. Queen Victoria did her best to pick it up and to back up the Australian mines, but by the 1920s it had become almost declassé. Now that opals have come back into fashion, we are finding that the really big beauties are hard to get.

Even its traducers could never say that it was not beautiful. Pliny, one feels by his description of the opal, really preferred it to the emerald, but as it is markedly less hard he had to place it after the emerald. He described it charmingly: "for in them you shall see the living fire of the ruby, the glorious purple of the amethyst, the sea-green of the emerald, all glittering together in an incredible mixture of light." He also spoke of what in his time was called the "opalus": "There exists today a gem of this kind, on account of which the Senator Nonius was proscribed by Antony. Seeking safety in flight, he took with him of all his possessions this ring alone (as large as a hazelnut) and valued at 2,000,000 sesterces." One wonders where it was mined, India or Hungary.

Albertus Magnus (1193–1280) had his say on another opal. The one he describes was set in the imperial crown of the Holy Roman Empire. "The Orphanus is a stone which is in the crown of the Holy Roman emperor and none like it has ever been seen; for this very reason it is called orphanus. It is of a subtle vinous tinge, and its hue as though pure white snow flashed and sparkled with the color of ruddy wine and was overcome by this radiance. It is said to guard the royal honor." (One feels on reading this description that a great copywriter was lost to the world.) The "orphanus" too very likely came from Hungarian mines. To own the crown with the orphanus meant kingship. A man could be as royal as he pleased and have precisely the right ancestors for the job, but without actually possessing the orphanus his chances were nil. Much thievery, one imagines, and some murders, occurred to get hold of it, for its significance was even greater than its value.

During the Middle Ages the opal received a new name, "ophthalmos," which means "the eye." It was offered as a guaranteed panacea for all eye troubles—and what is more could render you invisible. It was then that it became the patron stone of thieves. It was then, too, that it began to acquire its doubtful reputation. The mental association of an "eye" stone, in times when the evil eye was accepted as calmly as the price of pigs, was inevitable. So a stone which started out as beneficent became maliferous. Still it had its adherents. It was credited with the ability to foretell disaster. During the plague in Venice (1433) when fever struck its wearer, it was said to flare up strongly to give warning. Extraordinarily faithful, it often "died" with its owner. In the time of Queen Elizabeth I the famous Dr. Batman wrote: "Optallio is called Oppalus also, and this stone bredeth only in Inde and is deemed to have as many virtues as hiews and colors."

Time moved on, and it was in the sixteenth and seventeenth centuries that the opal was struck a mortal blow and became a stone accursed. Individual stones have been accursed before: the Koh-i-noor, the Hope Diamond, the Arabian Curse—but the whole opal family was damned out of hand. There may have been a practical reason

124   The German imperial crown containing the "Orphanus" stone. Woodcut, 1483.

for this. During the great days of craftsmen, the stonecutter and the lapidary were responsible to the owner and goldsmith for the stone. There was no industrial insurance then. If the cutter lost too much weight from a diamond, if he chipped a ruby, made a mistake in the cutting of an emerald, he had to replace the stone. Opals, being unevenly hydrated, are fragile and can fracture or scratch quite easily. The cleverest cutter, thinking perhaps that he had some kind of multicolored jasper or moonstone on his wheel, would see it suddenly and for no apparent reason come apart in his hands.

In those days nothing was known of the chemistry of the opal or of its tricky dehydration problem. A stone was a stone to the cutter, and only the opal, and sometimes the topaz and emerald, behaved really outrageously. Yet, in spite of being blacklisted, the opal continued on its way, beautiful, passionate, and fighting for its brief life. For the opal too knows death of a kind. Time withers it, which is why there are no really ancient opals. In some hundreds of years it will crack, splinter, break, and return to dust—which was another unexpected factor that horrified the early lapidaries and gave it one further push down the road to ostracism.

The great strike at Lightning Ridge in New South Wales occurred during the reign of Queen Victoria, and she backed up her far-flung interests nobly. She gave opals to her children, she wore them, Prince Albert gave them to her, and one imagines she had a good many "samples" presented to her from appreciative mining interests. If she didn't love them she certainly put on a good front, and the opal, in England at least, had a brief, happy vogue. And then the beautiful Queen Alexandra came to the throne. She was a woman of fashion and had very grand and very orthodox views of royal regalia. The huge opal parure, complete with bracelets and combs and stomachers, magnificently designed and with sizable diamond settings, was emptied of the opals, and rubies were set in their place. The opals are still there, among the crown jewels, and still unset.

Because they are so "other" and so unboringly beautiful, opals continued to be worn by women, particularly after the 1905 discovery of the black opal, but they were definitely out of fashion and a rather trite aura of unluckiness continued to hang over them, although no one could ever say what they were unlucky about. There came a time when the average person couldn't tell a blue opal from a butterfly's wing. Now once more they are being set with diamonds, or heaped together as earrings, or centered in a jeweled pin. No stone can daunt them, for they can match the best, tint for tint, and still find strength for laughter and dancing.

Pearl **XIX**

*P*earl: possibly from the Greek for "pear," later from the Latin *perla,* although Pliny called the big ones "unio" and the lesser pearls "margarita," from the Persian "child of the sea." Salt-water, fresh-water, and cultured: organic substance formed in oysters or mussels, with a hardness of around 2½ or 3½ to 4½.

What to look for: size, symmetry, luster, and color.

Of course the pearl doesn't belong here at all. It is organic and not a mineral, although like us it has minerals in it. Yet leaving the pearl out of the roster of most precious things would make the list look ridiculous. For the pearl, lacking the fire of the diamond, the wild life of the opal, the bland serenity of the moonstone, is a subtle and distilled version of all three. Because of its evasive beauty and intangible colors, its delicate hints of hidden mysteries, it is the Eros and Agape of jewels; the most earthly and the most unearthly. No one says, "She is a ruby among women," and no one says, "This is a sapphire of great price." It is the pearl that gets these accolades—with its gentle emanations and rather spiritual loveliness.

A pearl set or in a necklace gives a very different impression from a pearl separate and alone. Solitary and unpierced, a pearl seems oddly complete: a small, self-contained, self-absorbed, light-enveloped universe. Pierced and strung, the most beautiful pearl loses its separateness at once and becomes a smiling part of an indivisible whole.

In Europe, for some reason, the pearl necklace has always been worn primarily by women. Men have, in their time, worn great pearl-studded ruby collars, or shoulder knots dripping emerald and sapphire and pearls; pearls have been sewn to their tunics, hung from their hat ornaments, embroidered on a coat, or set in an order worn as studs or pinned in an ascot. They have even been worn as earrings (Charles I wore one all his life), but pearl necklaces, no. In India, on the other hand, men to this day wear necklaces of very manly sized pearls, often the treasure of a noble house. In fact, by and large, the great pearls remain in India, where they are worn with affection and understanding by maharajas or the mighty in breath-catching size and superb quality— and where else could one find a carpet of pearls ten feet long, or a winding pearl sash with an emerald fringe?

Pearls are formed of calcium carbonate, conchiolin, and water. Along with quartz, the pearl is probably the oldest "jewel" known to man. Any one of certain of our ancestors had only to be hungry and inquisitive to find them. He must have pried open the shell, or broken it on a bit of rock—as this was probably even before he discovered flint—and looked with great amazement at the shimmering silvery sphere. How long before he discovered it was not good to eat? How long before he discovered he could put a hole through it? Before that, did he just roll the iridescent balls in his great hand?

It was not until the twentieth century that the truth about the formation of the pearl was soundly established. Down the ages there had been some splendid suggestions, about on a par with the theory that a pale balas spinel was an "unripe" ruby. Pearls were raindrops that fell into an open mollusk. They were the undischarged eggs of the mollusk. In 1554 an unromantic theorist decided pearls were gallstones. Finally, in 1904, a French scientist called Boutan came as close to the truth as makes no difference. It is now known that an intrusion (which can be as small as a germ) in the mantle of the mollusk causes increased development of the epithelial cells, which begin to discharge nacre to surround the irritation.

Sometimes it is a germ, sometimes a foreign body, and in the case of the cultured pearl a definitely inserted "seed," which starts the organism "sealing up" the intruder. Often when an oriental pearl is X-rayed, so small is the intrusion that no foreign body of any kind can be seen; the pearl is pure nacre right to the center.

While luster is a matter of temperature, by and large it is the water itself, or some substance in the water, that gives the pearl its color. Different bodies of water produce different-colored pearls, and a pearl connoisseur can often tell just by looking whence the pearl came. There are always unusual examples, of course, but speaking generally the Persian Gulf is apt to produce a creamy pearl, Australia a white one with a green or blue tone. Panama can produce a golden brown, and Mexico a reddish-brown and black. From Ceylon come pearls with a particularly rosy cast, from Japan creamy pearls or white pearls with a greenish cast. The Burmese pearls are white with a pink orient.

The lustrous iridescence of a pearl is called its "orient" and is the result of two optical phenomena: light breaking up over the thin layers forming the surface of the pearl and the refraction of light reflecting back from the uneven layers as they meet at the surface. Translucency in the outer layers is what is wanted, for nothing is deader looking than a chalky pearl.

During the 1920s and 1930s, between the advent of the cultured pearl and the Depression, the oriental pearl business all but came to a standstill, but with odd results. Those who could afford it took to cultured pearls, and those who could not wore imitation pearls openly and boldly and without pretense. As a consequence, women began wearing more pearls of one kind or another than ever before, and what is more, they were far larger.

Prior to the 1920s there had been the add-a-pearl necklace, seed pearls, and countless lustrous strands of graduated pearls, which were the great wedding present to a wife or daughter, or on the birth of a first child, or for an anniversary. Beautiful, luminous, and expensive as those pearls were, by today's standard they were very small. Pearls are measured in millimeters (though weighed in grains) rather than carats, and the millimeter measures the diameter. Barring the pearls of the very rich or royal, the large center pearl in the average handsome necklace was eight to twelve millimeters.

Be it said, no pearl can grow to enormous size and hold its perfect roundness. If the pearl is too long in the mollusk it begins to distort: the nacre, unavoidably, spreads unevenly, and the result is a baroque pearl. These can be quite beautiful (and Renaissance jewelers used them to perfection), but they can never have the highborn look of a shimmering perfect sphere.

The cultured pearl was not "invented," as one might suppose, by Messrs. Mikimoto, Nishikawa, or Misi in the early twentieth century but by an unsung genius in China in the thirteenth century. To be sure, those early efforts did not produce the round and iridescent shapes of today, but the introduction of a bit of lead or mother-of-pearl or even bone into the mollusk caused the outraged oyster to spread nacre over the intrusion—and it *was* a cultured pearl. Today it would be called a "blister pearl": one which adheres to the shell and must be cut out, and which is covered with nacre only on the top. It is a far cry from today's subtleties and perfections, but one might as well give the Chinese credit for that too, along with paper and gunpowder.

Today the art of "seeding" and cultivating the pearl has become a science, an art, and an industry. The Japanese are still the best technicians in the world, and they teach their secrets to no one. But these trained men have now wandered far from Japanese waters. While the majority of cultured pearls still come from Japan, the Burmese oyster is larger, and so are those from Australia and the South Seas. The larger the oyster, the larger the pearl. Q.E.D., the Japanese technicians are now farming pearls in all of those places as well as Japan. The mother-of-pearl "seed" is usually one millimeter less than actual pearl size—except in the case of an inferior pearl, where the bigger the pearl the bigger the mother-of-pearl bead and the thinner the layer of nacre.

The Japanese waters are colder, which adds luster to a pearl; the Burmese waters are warmer and this adds nacre to the pearl, and also—because of the larger size of the mollusk—dimension. A great jeweler in New York has a collection of these huge, smooth, rosy-white Burmese pearls, the largest of which was 16 millimeters. Alas, the price is what the Robber Barons paid for orientals. On the other hand, these are far larger and uniform in size, which is today's fashion. The Japanese pearl can be spectacularly beautiful, but it rarely grows to more than ten millimeters—a fact, however, which makes it more "buyable," and one's grandmother in any event would have thought this size enormous.

Pearls, cultured or natural, grow at varying rates of speed, depending in part on how long they stay in the oyster and what the temperature of the water is, and in part on the energy and output of the individual oyster. It is rather difficult to think of oysters' having individuality and personality, but the cultured pearl man knows for a fact that they do. A number of oysters of identical size and habitat are seeded identically, and and some oysters respond and some, one might say, simply go on relief.

The pearl is quite soft, varying between 2½ and a rare 4½, and in time, as all organic things must, it dies. Efforts are made to "bring them back": sometimes they are treated chemically, sometimes they are peeled in the hope that another layer of iridescence lies just beneath. Some jewelers suggest bathing them in sea water, some jewelers are horrified by the suggestion. The old theory of wearing pearls to "keep them alive" is also disputed. Some say it is the oil in the skin that helps, some say the acid present in the skin is destructive, some say the oxygen in the air is helpful, and that pearls kept *too* long in an airless safe deposit box can begin to elongate. Whatever one chooses to believe, the fact remains that after a good long life they die. The average pearl necklace should have a lustrous life of a minimum of a hundred and fifty years, but a number of historic pearls have survived far longer, as if their destiny was stronger than their mortality. There are a few, admittedly in pretty bad shape but still showing flecks of iridescence, from ancient Persian tombs, from Toltec and Aztec graves, and Byzantine and Greek findings, and from Egypt hundreds of years B.C. Some are badly battered and no longer look like real pearls. They look more like mother-of-pearl, or even like steel beads, but there are some which have apparently found a fountain of youth and continue on with a luminous disregard for time.

The Greeks loved pearls so much they even hung them in the pierced ears of marble statues, and no Roman matron of any standing at all would dream of being without dangling pearl earrings. Some pearls from the seventh and eighth centuries are still shimmering faintly. The great drops, the Pellagrine and the Perragrine, have come down the centuries smooth and gleaming. Catherine de' Medici's long ropes and drops seem to be immortal, for they are still about, still being worn, and perhaps still have further adventures ahead. Their history is long, their story laced with history, their beauty unquenched.

130

The Great Ropes
of Catherine

Slowly, dreamily, lulled by the gentle motion of silent swaying tides, the pearls grew large, luminous, and round and took their luster from the southern sea . . . and all was still until the sudden upward wrench, the blaze of light, and the clever judging fingers of the pearl merchants. Matched and pierced and threaded on gold wire (the pear shapes set aside), the pearls became a rope. Then wrapped in silk and blackness, jostled by a camel's rolling gait, they crossed a new salt sea and arrived in Rome.

First they came into the nervous hands of Pope Clement VII, that most unlikely nephew of Lorenzo the Magnificent. His were the hands that played with pontifical seals while Henry VIII roared for an answer about Catherine, that were tense when Charles V held him prisoner after the "German Fury" sack of Rome in 1527, and that shook with rage when he crowned that selfsame Charles Emperor in 1529.

And then in 1533, a year before he died, Pope Clement gave the pearls as Princely-Popely gift to his fourteen-year-old kinswoman Catherine on her marriage to the second son of Francis I of France, who later became King Henri II. The marriage must have been needful to Pope Clement. To pay for the wedding he pawned the biggest diamond in his tiara and made the gift of the pearls as well: six ropes of them and twenty-five teardrops, known as "the biggest and finest ever seen."

Catherine was Lorenzo the Magnificent's great-granddaughter, with flesh that surged with such ambition it must have made the pearls pulse at her throat. She wore them constantly, the great ropes hanging, the drops and single spheres on her cap or sewn to her dress. The pearls were close to her and would have felt the thwarted rage that blotched her skin and made claws of her hands, the rage that never reached the full protruding eyes—as she was forced to live with carefully studied insult, public neglect, to see the jewels of France (but never the pearls) hung upon Diane de Poitiers, and who received as her only mark of favor from the King—syphilis. She was not born to patience, but she acquired its semblance. Perhaps she had hoped to be strong, regal, and wise, to be allowed to triumph over her lack of blue blood. But in a few years' time she had become a sly manipulator, vengefully clever. Her hot pride grew cold and venomous. After that day of the Tournament when her husband Henri fell, pierced by a lance through the eye, she hoped to rule—for their young Francis was so boyish

CATHARINA · D ✦ VXOR · REGIS · GALLOR · II · HENRICI · REGIS · FRANC · REGINA

(*Left:*) Catherine de' Medici.

(*Right:*) Mary Queen of Scots.

and so malleable. But this was not to be. Francis married young Mary, Queen of Scots, and, a little mad from his father's gift perhaps, turned from his mother to Mary's clever uncles, the De Guises, and they ruled, totally.

Catherine gave the great ropes to Mary as a wedding gift. A bribe? A hope? A rare moment of affection? And so the pearls left that throat, already thickening at forty. They escaped forever the touch of the woman who later set the moment for the Massacre of Saint Bartholomew ahead an hour, to make sure that it took place: who tried to assassinate old Coligny, failed, but saw to it that he was the first one killed upon that day and his body dragged about for dogs to eat Would the pearls have survived the flesh of a woman whose hatred of her son Francis grew daily, until she openly rejoiced when his sad, mad little life came to an end when he was sixteen? His brother,

133

Charles IX, came to the throne then. As he was only ten years old, she came to power as Regent at last, and she wore balas rubies and other pearls, and then when he died fourteen years later, her last son, Henri III, ascended the throne at the age of twenty-three. Sometimes she controlled Henri and sometimes she did not. She lived to see him refuse even to consider marriage with that "heretic" Elizabeth of England, and to see him die, childless, by an assassin's hand, and Henry of Navarre ascend the throne. But the pearls had fled from her long since.

From 1559 they rested on young Mary's neck, who had such a happy, flighty pulse, and movements so quick the great ropes swung for all their weight. They were there, tumbling to her hips, the teardrops in her cap, when Francis died, and she was Dowager Queen, and just eighteen.

Then Mary was summoned home to Scotland. The De Guises were in disfavor, she a cipher now, and so in 1561 she sailed—sadly—for they say as long as the light lasted her eyes were fast on France. The pearls went to Scotland, in a casket lined with velvet and smelling of sandalwood. John Knox hated them and thought they looked like rosaries. She tried to reason with him, to cajole, but she had only the deft and graceful vocabulary of the court to meet his strong, crass mind.

The pearls knew the velvet of young Darnley's tunic, the leather of Bothwell's—and perhaps they knew the dark cloth of Rizzio. The baby James clutched them, and she should have read an omen in his hand, but life was too full of terrors to look for future troubles. And the pearls lived with it all: the fear, the passion, the defeats, the tempers and tears, and possibly sick cold guilt, and, finally, abdication. They knew the careful hands of Mary Seaton and Mary Beaton and Mary Flemming and Mary Livingstone—the ladies in waiting to the Queen. And then she went to England—to disgrace, imprisonment, humiliation, foolish decisions, and the wild hope that Elizabeth would name her heir, as one man said he would come to her standard, then turned to London, and another said he would, then stayed at home—until at last she snatched at straws and let herself be tangled into treasonable and pathetic plots. The ropes, the drops, the moonlit spheres were long since packed away in darkness as Mary went off to prison and to death, and James her son, now grown, stood by Elizabeth's judgment and said he "didn't object" and that he "quite understood," and turned his head away and was biddable, and clung, obsequious, to his heirdom.

Elizabeth bought the pearls. She got them from Murray, the Regent of Scotland, and at her own price, three thousand pounds. She ran them through her thin imperious hands, perhaps letting them rattle softly on an oak table, and told herself that she had bought them for the glory of the crown. And yet she must have thought long thoughts. "To punish treason is right and proper. The rack, the ax—there should be no pity for traitors—only death. To tear my England . . . that's a crime and punishable. And yet they say when she was . . . when she died, her wig fell off and her hair was gray, for all her girlish ways. Two old women fighting for a crown. But the crown was *mine*.

Elizabeth I of England wearing the ropes of Catherine.

Still, had she won she would have worn these pearls as Queen of England, so that was their destiny all the time. This one looks rather dull. I'll have it off, and give it to some fool as a sign of favor."

The pearls lay in great ropes against the thin flushed skin, rattled on the jeweled stomacher; the drops stood upright on a giant ruff and hung from her ears. Elizabeth loved jewels and, one way or another—by trickery, default, or just plain honest purchase—she built the finest crown jewels of the Western world. There were some complaints: Dom Antonio of Portugal insisted right to his death that she had cheated him, taken the Portuguese crown jewels that he had pawned with her for English help, and then withheld the help, and held the jewels. Henry IV too used her as pawnbroker to raise money for troops, raised sixty thousand crowns on the jewels of Navarre, but when his agent, Segur, went to redeem them somehow the price was three hundred thousand crowns—and crying angrily she would not be swindled, she kept the jewels until she died.

The pearls left that fiery subtle spirit for the strongbox of that chilling man, James I. Perhaps his early life undid him, for even as King he pleased few. The Catholics felt he had betrayed his mother's party; his attempt toward a Spanish marriage made the Protestants hysterical. The Addled Parliament was in his reign, and the name suited him even better. He loved dry theory and theological debate, and Anne of Denmark enough to marry her against the wishes of Elizabeth. For all that, in history he gets the credit for the King James Version, the founding of Jamestown, and of course the impeachment of Francis Bacon. He wrote some books, gathered some jewels (the Sancy was one), but the pearls—which may have stirred some guilt in his dry heart—he gave to his daughter Elizabeth on her marriage to Frederick of Bohemia in 1613.

So Pope Clement VII's lustrous pearls left England, and lay happily on the flesh of that beautiful girl all Europe called "The Queen of Hearts." Her husband's soubriquet, sad to say, was derisive. He was called "The Winter King," for that was the duration of his reign. At the battle of White Mountain—the first of the Thirty Years' War, really—he lost, betrayed perhaps by the lack of support from his father-in-law, James I, and the do-nothing behavior of the much-talk Protestant Union. And so in 1620 Elizabeth and Frederick fled to Holland and had thirteen children . . . and the pearls.

One daughter was Sophia. She married the Elector of Hanover, and their son, when the good Queen Anne died, childless but beloved, became England's George the First. His wife Sophia Dorothea (the daughter of Duke George William of Brunswick-Lüneburg) perhaps had the pearls, but, as her mother-in-law loathed her, perhaps not. If she wore them, she had small joy of them, for hers was a wretched marriage, but it is possible that they shimmered and trembled at her throat when her lover Count Königsmark was murdered—and when her marriage was annulled and she was put in prison. All England hated George. The man was a foreigner, spoke an ungainly tongue, understood nothing, and had German mistresses. The South Sea Bubble and the Jacob-

Elizabeth of Bohemia, after the ropes came into her possession. Portrait by Daniel Myters (detail).

ite Uprisings of 1715 exploded in his time, and he loathed England and wished he were in Germany, and did in fact spend as much time there as he could while keeping the English crown. Meanwhile, the pearls were idle, waiting for another queenly neck.

With the destinies of Great Britain and Hanover so closely wrought, the great pearls may have traveled back and forth. Sophia Dorothea's son was George II, and he was better disposed to England. He set the pearls upon the shoulders of his clever wife, Caroline. She, perhaps looping their delicate lengths across her bosom, wheedled her George into many wise decisions such as backing the Whigs and appointing Robert Walpole. Perhaps Caroline also suggested how conspicuously and *nobly* gallant it would appear to lead his men into battle. He did, at Dettinger in 1743, and was the last monarch to perform that kingly act.

The huge single spheres now lived together, strung into a great necklace but

137

always to feel the chill of the north, never again to know the sun of the Persian Gulf, or spring in Rome.

Then Caroline died, and George II, and when their grandson George III came to the throne, his wife had the pearls. (Were they among those in the Ramsay portrait?) Poor, good, plain Charlotte Sophia bore George fifteen children, and stood by him in the years of his madness. He lost the Colonies and lived too long—at least for his son's liking. The Regent snarled himself in debt, married Maria Fitzherbert, denied it publicly, and then, to make himself look better, married the unfortunate Caroline. Her tenure was quite brief, the scandal shattering, the truth veiled and, some say, subject to the King's wishes. The pearls were rather idle at that time. George IV ruled only ten years, but during his lifetime Hanover was made a kingdom at the Congress of Vienna in 1814 and so for a while he wore two crowns—and the pearls belonged to which? He died in 1830 and was succeeded by his brother William IV, who married Adelaide. The pearls by this time were called the Hanoverian Pearls.

When William died, Victoria succeeded, but the Hanoverians wanted no woman for a ruler and had a very careful, pointed law to that effect. So came about the dissolution of the crowns. Ernest Augustus, the last son of George III, was King of Hanover, and Victoria got England. The pearls? In 1837 Ernest Augustus began demanding the return of the Hanoverian jewels and was most specific about a necklace of thirty-seven full moons. Nothing but stilted wrangling came of it, and a coolness developed between the two courts. Finally, in 1843, King Ernest Augustus put on his traveling boots and came himself to England. He spoke very pointedly. So Queen Victoria widened her great blue eyes and said, "But of *course*," and "How shocking this delay," and promptly turned it over to the law. That, of course, took years. In the end, as one great, perfectly matched pearl looks rather like another—just as in the fairy tale where the prince tries to discover the True Princess—poor Ernest Augustus could not pick them out. At last, in 1858, twenty-one years after he started asking, and six years after he died, the case was settled. Hanover got a necklace, and a splendid one, but which if any of those silent, smiling spheres had known the glad and sorrowing beauty of fourteen queens?

Queen Victoria, with Prince Albert in 1854.

Amethyst, Citrine, and Other Quartz

XXI

A pink tourma-
line, with a pa-
nache of diamonds.

Quartz: from the old German *quarz*. Hexagonal system with the hardness of 7.

What to look for: color, transparency, absence of flaws in crystalline quartz, which includes amethyst, citrine, cairngorm, rock crystal, rose and gold quartz, cat's-eye, tiger's-eye and hawk's-eye (both chatoyant stones), and chalcedony. The crypto-crystalline quartz includes carnelian, chrysoprase, plasma, bloodstone, agate, onyx, sardonyx, and jasper, and in them one looks for color, luster, and polish.

Quartz is a huge and beautiful family and the most common of all solid minerals. Between the two varieties, quartz covers nearly every degree of transparency and every shade of color.

It would be a book in itself if one were to consider the whole cryptocrystalline family, so only the crystalline variety is discussed here. Most of it is very well known. Rose quartz has ranked for centuries with jade, lapis lazuli, and malachite as an ex-quisite medium for *objets d'art*. Rose quartz can on rare occasions show asterism, and "starred" stones have been used for jewelry. Rose quartz can also—even more rarely—be entirely transparent. When this happens collectors and curators call each other up breathlessly, but the general public is apt to look at it and just say, "Oh," for a good deal of its gentle, beautiful color is due to inclusions.

Rock crystal, along with amethyst, was considered by the ancients to be a precious stone. In fact, rock crystal was the "diamond" of all the years before Christ and con-tinued to be generally confused with the diamond right up to the Middle Ages. It was also considered to be ice, frozen past recall, but Pliny was rather dubious about this. Iris quartz, which is rock crystal, really, with water or air inclusions, is beautifully iridescent; the Empress Josephine had a bright and shimmering parure of it. Next to the precious chrysoberyl, Oriental cat's-eye, the quartz cat's-eye is the most feline of the chatoyant stones: a dark olive or a yellowish stone with the line in a lighter shade. However, by far the most important gem of the quartz family is the amethyst.

Amethyst: from the Greek *amethystos*, "not drunken." Six-sided crystals with a hardness of 7.

140

What to look for: strength or gaiety of color, purple to violet, violet to red; flawlessness, even distribution of color.

Where found: everywhere that quartz is found, but today's best source is Brazil. Also Uruguay, Siberia, Ceylon, India, Madagascar, Persia, Mexico, Maine, New Hampshire, Pennsylvania, North Carolina, and the Lake Superior district.

Amethyst, "not drunken," was an implication taken literally for thousands of years by that not inconsiderable group which always takes everything literally. As a consequence, drinking goblets were made of it, amulets were firmly clutched on several millennia of Saturday nights, and it was often cursed as a false amethyst—the morning after.

But if, for the word "drunken," you choose to read "intoxicated," the meaning can enlarge and go up a level or two. It then meant that the amethyst represented those qualities which would keep-a man from worldly "intoxication": keep him from falling headlong into life, error, tempers, and infatuations. In that case it would represent detachment, judgment, self-discipline, and high standards. It makes morse sense that way and suits the old quotation, "By its charm it giveth good understanding."

Amethyst is the stone of bishops and Bacchus, a fine case of symbols making strange bedfellows. The Bacchus legend came first and the association is easy—grapes. The legend had to do with just one more temper display by the gods. Bacchus, affronted over some slight to his altar, swore that he would loose his wolves on the next mortal who passed by. It happened to be a beautiful maiden on her way to make an offering at the temple of Artemis. When Artemis heard the maiden's shrieks she hastily turned her into solid crystal—not even pausing to ask which form of death she would prefer. When Bacchus saw how beautiful she was, and what a lovely transparent character she had, he felt so sorry that he poured over her a libation of wine. And the result was "the amethyst."

Amethyst is lovely in the raw. Its crystals, grouped together in varying heights, lift airily and look like a dawn-touch view of fairy-tale skyscrapers. They usually act as linings for agate geodes and sometimes grow in mineral veins or in granite rocks. For the most part they are pale and watery looking, showing their close kinship with rock crystal all too clearly, but there, at the tip or to one side, is the sudden sharp glow of that imperial purple. What gives them their proud color is in dispute. Many say it is manganese. Others say it must be an organic substance, as amethysts are subject to change or loss of color when subjected to intense heat.

The most coveted amethysts came from Russia and were called Siberian amethysts. The best amethysts are still apt to be called Siberian, but now it donates only color and not the place of origin. (The Kashmir sapphire is in the same stiuation. Very likely it comes from Burma or Thailand, but is of that cornflower blue to which Kashmir gave its name.) Brazil is the great source of amethysts today, with Uruguay second.

Just as the ruby and sapphire are both corundum, and the emerald and the aquamarine are both beryl, so the amethyst, citrine, and the cairngorm are all quartz. The citrine can start out in life as an amethyst and then be heat-treated and thus changed to a high lovely yellow. On the other hand, the cairngorm, so dear to the heart of the Scot, is smoky quartz, a misty yellow or soft brown. Great in the handle of a dirk, it is not as acceptable to ladies as the citrine or amethyst.

Oddly enough, amethyst devotees are sometimes rather defensive in their passion for these proud purple crystals, as if they felt that the world must think them lacking to waste their devotion on stones not truly great. Perhaps they would become more assured if they reminded themselves that as late as the sixteenth century this born-to-the-purple Russian quartz cost as much as diamonds and was equally valued. Before the great South American mines were opened fine amethysts were scarce. As the stone was both scarce and beautiful at that time, it was set with its peers—rubies, sapphires, emeralds, and diamonds—in almost every ancient European crown, scepter, orb, and sword.

The history of amethysts is long, as prehistoric graves, Chaldean seals, Egyptian carvings, Greek intaglios, Roman signets bear witness. A zodiac stone from the beginning, the amethyst was number nine on the Breastplate of the High Priest and number twelve of the Foundation Stones of the New Jerusalem, and because of its place in the last two the stone has been included in the crown of almost every Christian king. The twelve stones, which once had definite symbolic meanings, have been repeated—though what they symbolized perhaps is long forgotten—from the covering of the King of Tyre to the crown of William the Conqueror and that of Good Queen Bess, to the teen-ager's scarab bracelet.

It was not until 610 A.D. that the bishop's ring became a symbol of dignity. Prior to that it had been a personal signet ring. Innocent III decreed "a ring of pure gold, set with stones, not engraved." He had good cause to deny engraving. At that time, and for many centuries to come, the great thing was the discovery of old—and, of course, pagan—engraved stones. Rome, having imported, enslaved, or bribed every clever Greek gem carver they could lay their hands on, was the world center for the intaglio stone: in sapphire, jasper, emerald, carnelian, lapis lazuli—in fact, in anything soft enough to work. Thousands of these delicately engraved stones were unearthed during the ensuing centuries, most of them representing Greek or Roman gods. The intaglio stone was promptly put in a new setting and Christianized out of hand. The monks of Durham, for instance, changed Jupiter to Saint Oswald by the simple expedient of saying very loudly that that was who he was. The number of times Aphrodite and Eros became the Mother Mary and the Infant Jesus can't be counted. Bearded satyrs became Saint Peter, Dionysus became John the Baptist. Hermes, too, in a flash of winged feet, became Saint Michael, and a most beautiful intaglio of Leda and the Swan ended up set in a reliquary holding a tooth of the Apostle Peter, with no explanation offered.

To misquote Robert Graves: "Conquering gods their image take from the gods they captive make."

As the amethyst is the only purple stone of note, with a gentle, almost noble magnificence, it is not surprising that it was so revered. If the South American mines had never been discovered, would it have remained in the hierarchy of rubies and diamonds? Possibly its comparative softness is against it, but its color is unique.

Perhaps today not enough imagination is being used in enhancing the amethyst. It usually gets a gold setting, or at best a small diamond one, or a circle of tiny pearls. Yet an amethyst with a bright green emerald or a blue turquoise is very exciting.

The amethyst kept its high place in the world of fashion even after the great mines of South America began pouring them onto the market. All through the eighteenth and nineteenth centuries it was well in the forefront. Queen Charlotte in the late eighteenth century had a magnificent necklace which was valued at the time at two thousand pounds. Today it is valued at one hundred pounds. It was the twentieth century that somehow pulled down the character of this splendid stone.

The spectacular amethyst is, of course, always in demand, fashionable or not; the amethyst with no hint of mauve or eggplant, that is neither streaked nor watery, that has the same quality of velvetiness as the best sapphire, and the glow of a ruby . . . or of a lighter hue, that will leap with a vivid, bright violet light. While an amethyst cannot show fire, it can show dichroism. Properly cut, it can sometimes twinkle and shoot off sparks of red and violet, startling and beautiful.

When the amethyst was at its most expensive it was used the most lavishly. One of the twenty thrones (each for a different season or ritual) in the Russian treasury was the one sent to Tsar Alexis in 1660, made by the apparently abandoned hand of an Armenian called Zachary Saradorow. It was set with eight hundred and seventy-six diamonds and one thousand two hundred and twenty-three amethysts, and at a time when amethysts were on a par with diamonds! The so-called Persian Throne, which was a gift from the Shah of Persia to Ivan IV, was set with one thousand three hundred and twenty-five rubies and hyacinths (zircons), five hundred and thirty-nine turquoises, quantities of pearls, sapphires, peridots, fifteen unusually handsome amethysts —and some false emeralds! With such lavish bejeweling, why cheat on the emeralds? A covetous passion for emeralds on the part of the Shah which at the last moment made him unable to part with them, or an honest jeweler's honest mistake?

The amethyst wears well, polishes well, holds its color, and does not break if you look it at. It is a stalwart stone with an august heritage. Best for a fine amethyst is the antique or cushion cut, or else the step cut, which give additional sparkle. When judging an amethyst you should look through the back of the stone. If there is some streaking, it should be slight and towards the edges. As fine amethysts are always available, it is worthwhile having the little patience necessary to find a really splendid stone, full of life, stanch of color.

XXII

Spinel

Spinel: from the Greek *spine*, meaning "thorn." Cubic system, octahedral crystals with a hardness of 8.

What to look for: transparency, color.

What to avoid: grayed, very dark, or flabby colors, flaws.

Where found: Ceylon, Burma, Cambodia, Thailand, India, Madagascar, Australia, and Afghanistan.

The spinel has a certain scarcity, especially in crystals of over six or seven carats. It is redoubtably hard, just below the ruby and sapphire and above the emerald, and so takes a high polish and can have brilliance. It has a good luster and is found in a gamut of colors: red, orange, pink, blue, and violet, as well as brown and black.

It used to be right up there with the mighty, but today labors under the great disadvantage of too closely resembling the *more* precious ruby, sapphire, amethyst, etc. In the days when fine distinctions were not made, colored spinels played a major role, but always under another stone's name.

Yellow and green spinels are practically nonexistent in nature, and the colorless ones frequently seen are sure to be synthetic. Since about 1915 there have been many synthetic spinels—and very good they are, especially the pink. The violet and blue spinels are more frequent, but their weakness is that they do not quite achieve the color perfection of the stones they resemble: the sapphire and the amethyst. It is a great pity the spinel cannot be judged on its own beauty, which is considerable.

The blue spinel would be a fine stone indeed if the sapphire did not exist. It is a splendid dark, deep blue and has a certain cold steeliness that is quite exciting. Violet spinel is an altogether enchanting stone, sometimes a lilting violet, sometimes a fine dark orange-violet shade which looks as if it might turn the trick that an alexandrite does any minute, and there is a spinel that actually does—switching from a light, steely blue by day to a violet under artificial light.

The red spinel, however, is another story. It has always held a high position. It comes in a romantic range of reds and has, at different times, been given three names to describe these colors. Ruby spinel, a fine crimson red, which can be beautifully transparent, is handsome and important. In old lapidaries one reads of the "balas ruby" which covered all the rose and pink spinels. It is sometimes a purplish-rose-red and sometimes drifts up to a rather vivid pink. It has been a great favorite since Roman times. Rubicelle is the former name for the flaming orange-red stone, which when clear and brilliant is quite staggering in its unexpected beauty. These three stones, incidentally, represent the last three castes in the old Indian ruby "caste" system.

By the sixteenth century the Burmese and Indians had made the separation, but even those ruby lovers made errors, and, as spinel is so often found in company with corundum ruby and has been called the "Mother of Rubies," it is not surprising.

In Europe it was not until after the fourteenth century that the royal inventories began listing separately the Oriental ruby, "balas ruby," and spinel. The news did not travel fast, and occasionally a three-hundred-carat "balas ruby" went into pawn as a ruby, only to be turned away or valued at a fraction of what it had been valued at a few years before. It took a certain refinement of understanding to agree that a four-carat pigeon-blood Oriental ruby had a greater value than a three-hundred-carat balas ruby. As late as 1569, when Charles IX of France sent the five great rubies of France out to pawn, the valuers of the Duke of Florence announced that they were not Oriental rubies but balas, and paid poor Charles accordingly.

Almost every one of the great historical "rubies" that exist today is a spinel. All you have to do is see or read of their size, and the cat is out of the bag. The great Timur Ruby is a three-hundred-and-fifteen-carat spinel. The four-hundred-and-fifteen-carat "ruby" that tops the Russian Imperial Crown is a spinel. (It is the stone that Catherine I took from Prince Galzetine—who was executed in Siberia for bribery—and gloriously rich it still looks, its crimson and rose displayed in the Kremlin.)

There is the Black Prince's ring, still to be seen pulsing redly as the light strikes it, and the great rosy-red balas known as the Côte de Bretagne was part of the dowry of Anne de Bretagne when she married Charles VIII of France in 1491, a huge, rough, rosy stone that she wore as a pendant. Perhaps Anne still wore it when, as a widow, she married yet another king of France, Louis XII. In 1749 Louis XVI had it carved into a dragon and set in an Order. It was stolen in the robbery of the Garde-Meuble, but after a mysterious interim in Antwerp, it turned up again and landed at the Louvre, where, shorn of its old setting, it glows rosily, the most beguiling dragon of them all.

There is the big one-hundred-and-seventy-carat "balas ruby" which Henry V wore in his helm at Agincourt. "Once more unto the breach dear friends . . ." And it was already an old stone, for the Black Prince had taken it from Dom Pedro of Castille in 1397. And then, to make babes of them all, the death and destruction stone, the ruby-red spinel called Timur. Now there is a tale . . .

The Great Timur

XXIII

It was named Khiraj-i-Alam, "Tribute of the World," and it was huge and glower-ingly red, which was altogether suitable. Kings carved their names on it, in Persian, but using the curving Arab script:

> Akbar Shah
> Jehangir Shah
> Sahil Oiran Sani
> Alamgir Shah
> Badshah Ghazu Mahamad Farukh Siyar
> Ahmed Shar Duri-i-Duran

Three names besides these were cut out—for shame perhaps, for one at least was a patricide.

And later it was catalogued—on itself, thus: "This is the ruby among the twenty-five thousand jewels of the King of Kings—the Sultan Sahib Qiran, which in 1153, from the collection of jewels of Hindustan, reached this place." The place was Isfahan, and the year by our calendar was A.D. 1740.

The Timur was intimate to the longest bloodletting of any stone in history. For close to a millennium it watched the savage games of kings, noted their unconcealed pleasure in cruelty, saw greed that was senseless in its magnitude, patricide, fratricide, torture, and rapine.

Yet often these same kings were actively devout, knew poetry, and valued philos-ophy, and dearly loved a wife. With one hand they copied a Persian miniature or slid appreciative fingers over a Chinese vase, and with the other sharpened a pole for impaling a captive.

What slave brought the Timur to light nobody knows, or whether it was found half-polished in some stream, or taken from its rock and put to wheel. But its history probably began in the eleventh century when four Hindu dynasties ruled the Sultanate of Delhi. They were a weak, cruel line of kings, fond of sweet pulpy fruit, small wars, red and yellow stones, and building cities. In 1191 the last Sultan, Prithwi-raja, gave place to Muhammed of Ghor, a man of will, with strength to back it up, who swept from the West, conquered Delhi, and seized the jewels as loot. It was thus that the Muslim dynasties began.

In 1398 Mahmud Tughlak was Sultan when, once more from the West, came a certain man of Samarkand, known to some as Amir Timur, and to a million dead as Tamerlane. Mahmud fled, and after sacking Delhi, Timur raised there a pyramid of eighty thousand skulls. With hands that were rough and black around the nails, he carried away the "ruby" and renamed it "Timur." The howling Tartars galloped west, as they had galloped east, on shaggy foam-flecked ponies from the steppes. However, according to an artist of the time, the steed Tamerlane rode was a curveting beauty from Arabia.

The Timur traveled down the Timurid line, from son to son's son, sharing the sable setting for the crown with fleas and lice—from Tamerlane's fourth son, Shah Rukh, to his son, that good astronomer King, Mirza Ulugh Beg, who only ruled two years when he was killed by Abdul Latif, his own son.

Then the power of the Timurid line began to wane, and the Timur fell to the strong acquisitive hands of Abbas I of the Safari family, who ruled Persia until 1628. Abbas, whose chief wealth came from silk, was a shrewd trader, capable of making grand gestures when it was to his obvious gain. Thus, as a soft bribe he presented the Timur to the powerful Mogul Emperor Jehangir.

Jehangir was a relatively cheerful man, as Mogul emperors went, killing thousands fewer than most. He loved food and pearls and sport, Persian miniatures, Chinese paintings . . . and the Timur. It was Jehangir who had the stone engraved, and, when his beloved wife Mur Jehan remonstrated with him for "marring" it, answered, "This stone will more certainly hand down my name to posterity than any written history. The house of Timur may fall, but as long as there is a king this stone will be his." Because he was a man more proud than vain, in addition to his own name he had the name of his father cut, the great Akbar Shah, who had ruled from 1556 to 1605. His father was a most unusual man. Although illiterate, he had ears and eyes and understanding and he filled his court with Brahmins, Moslems, and Jesuits, to whom he listened attentively. He tried to make a synthesis of all three religions, a form of monotheism, but the great experiment died with him, for despite the fact that Jehangir was devoted to his father Akbar, he was even more devoted to orthodox Mohammedanism.

Jehangir had wide interests. He built the lovely mosque at Ispahan, gave trade privileges to the East India Company, and learned from its members news of the other world: of England and the great Elizabeth dead, of her successors James I and Charles I, of King Henry of Navarre, who said, "Every peasant should have a chicken in his pot every Sunday." Henry's concern for the common man must have shocked the lordly Jehangir as a most unseemly interest for a king.

And so, in 1627, the Timur came to Jehangir s son, the Shah Jehan, who built the

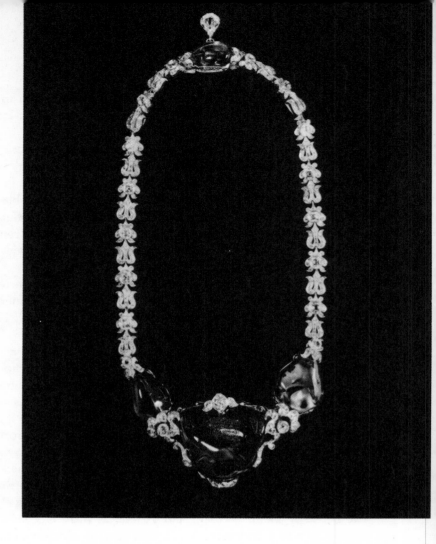

The Timur, set in a necklace which now belongs to Queen Elizabeth II. *(Far right:)* Detail, showing the inscription on the stone—the names of the successive owners.

Taj Mahal, the Pearl Mosque at Agra, and the Diwan-i-Am. In this audience hall the Peacock Throne was set (valued at six million golden crowns), on which, suspended from a chain, the Timur hung. On the stone Shah Jehan carved himself as the Second Tamerlane, or as it went in the subtle Persian manner, "Second Lord of the Auspicious Conjunction."

Shah Jehan was able, and he was cruel. He killed off all his male relatives to make the throne more secure—but who remembers this when looking entranced at that emblem of husbandly love, the Taj? Perhaps Jehan was fatalist enough, or wise enough in the ways of his forebears, not to be surprised when his third son, Aurangzeb, "World Shaker," cast him into jail, battled his brothers, and in 1627 took the Peacock Throne, the power, and the jewels. Aurangzeb was a paradox. He was violent, greedy for power, but he was also austere, scholarly, and devout. He had an iron claw which he wore like a glove for spontaneous disembowling. Yet he could be gentle enough to

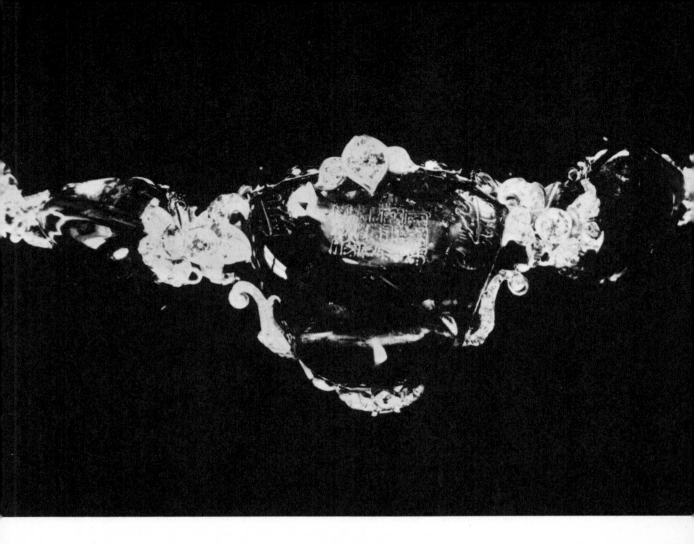

treat Tavernier with the utmost courtesy, and generous and trusting enough to let nim hold in his palm the Great Mogul, the legendary diamond known even then to half the world. Some like to say that the Great Mogul is the Orloff Diamond—and if by chance it is, this stone now glitters owlishly at the Kremlin, shaped like half an egg and faceted on three sides.

As the Timur hung on the Peacock Throne, two emperors came and went; but they were of small account, for the epic of the Moguls had been written. Now it was only a tale told fiercely by old men to the very young. The last Mogul was Emperor Mahamad Farukh Siyar, who reigned but five years, until 1718. He was frightened all the time, and when he fingered his stones his suspicious eye moved fearfully over his personal guard, and he prayed to Allah for peace.

Peace did not last long, for down from Persia swung Nadir Shah, and once again Delhi was put to the sack. In 1739 all the jewels and the Peacock Throne itself went back to Persia. The Timur was described at the time as "upwards of three fingers in breadth and nearly two in length," and it continued to be called the "Tribute of the World." And so it lay under the palm of Nadir Shah, a clever, wily, cruel man. He was so powerful that, as sometimes happens, total power corrupted him—totally—and he grew quite mad with fear and suspicion, even having the eyes of his own son put out. On one of his forays his personal bodyguard assassinated him, and a feeble son, poor Shah Shuja, stepped to the Peacock Throne. He proved no match for his adversaries, who finally seized him, blinded him, and continued to torture him with the purpose of finding out where he had hidden the Koh-i-noor, the Timur, and other jewels. Before Shah Shuja died of his inquisition, rescue came in the form of Ahmen Shah, of the Durani breed, who drove north from Afghanistan, released him, and as a reward, was "given" the Timur. Ahmen Shah held the stone for a short while, when once again down from the north the plunderers came, this time led by the Punjab warrior-king Ranjit Singh (whom Kipling would have invented if he hadn't already existed), who took the Timur—and the Koh-i-noor as well. Ranjit Singh customarily played at siding with the English in India, but suddenly he turned on them. This proved of no avail, and in 1849 he fell. By now the days of the Ranjit Singhs were over. Gold was being panned in California, Queen Victoria had ruled twelve years, *Dombey and Son* had just been published, and Napoleon III was on his way back to France. And so the East India Company in its gentle and orderly way "took possession" of the jewels in the Treasury of Lahore, and brought them back to England and their Queen.

For the first time, after centuries of male power, the Timur had entered the woman's world—an almost laughable fate, like Hercules forced to spin for Omphale. Timur, "Tribute of the World," that had glowered and glowed for Tamerlane, seen patricide, fratricide, impaling poles, and vultures darkening half a province, now lay meek as a moonstone at Queen Victoria's throat. And so today it rests, purged of its past, tamed of its wild ways, its crimson power stilled—all daintily set about with diamonds and centered in a necklace for the Queen's pleasure.

The Mogul Emperor Jehangir entertains Shah Abbas. Early seventeenth-century Mogul painting.

XXIV

Topaz

Topaz: named, according to Pliny, for the island Topazos in the Red Sea. A large family of the orthorhombic system with the hardness of 8.
What to look for: see below.
Where found: Brazil is today the best source of precious topaz.

In Brazil the discovery of a topaz deposit is greeted with especial joy, for there are those who think a tin mine even more beautiful than a topaz, and the presence of that stone often indicates the presence of tin ore.

The topaz, however, needs no tin mine to give it authority and prestige. This sunny colored crystal, which is harder than many emeralds and cleaves cleanly and has the glassy luster of the emerald or peridot, has lighted candles all through history. So rich and warm is its golden tone one hesitates to call it a pastel. The Egyptians knew it, as did the Indians, Greeks, Romans, Saxons, Franks, and Teutons. It was recorded as one of the twelve stones of the High Priest's Breastplate and the Foundation Stone of the New Jerusalem. All the generations of man have spoken lovingly and pridefully of the topaz. However, in those days any golden stone was apt to be called a topaz, and that, of course, applied to such stones as citrine quartz, yellow peridot, tourmaline, sapphire, zircon, chrysoberyl, etc. The list is endless, but somehow topaz got the mantle, and usually all the others sheltered under it.

It has always been popular in the East, where yellow stones are really appreciated, and both there and in Europe in earlier times it was set, without question of rank, with rubies, sapphires, and emeralds. As time wore on, however, it lost its high standing in the West, even though it stood just below rubies and sapphires in hardness and was capable of even brilliance. One can only conclude that for some mysterious reason the yellow stone does not succeed in the West. For all that, where ritual and symbol are part of the assemblage, the topaz is almost invariably present.

What is wanted in a precious topaz is purity—for it is a crystal prone to inclusions—and color and good cut, for one of the charms of the topaz is that it can achieve great ebullience. Fine stones are very rare, but even so there is no point in having other than a near-perfect stone, for it is such a clear golden shade and so beautifully transparent that it does not take much in the way of a feather or inclusion to spoil it. The best color is a light, dazzling gold with, perhaps, a hint of red.

The precious topaz deserves the best possible cut. Both the brilliant or the step cut are splendid for it. As it is so hard it takes a high polish, but poorly cut or badly proportioned it becomes a bit sad and sober-looking. If it has a light, high tint the crystal should have a certain depth to it. If it is on the dark, gold side the stone can be a little shallower. Either round or emerald cut are excellent for it, always providing the stone has perfect clarity and good color. The square cut can be lovely but presents certain hazards, for the corners of this cut make it vulnerable. Hard as the topaz is, a sharp blow can start a feather, and though the stone rarely breaks it is definitely marred.

Possibly the blue topaz is the best-known member of the family, other than the rare and precious yellow. It has clarity and intensity of color, higher pitched and more "pastel" than a light sapphire, and a lighter sky blue than most aquamarines. So lovely is the color that it is seen a good deal even in a poor state; cloudy, full of inclusions and flaws, cut cabochon. It is well worth the time of anyone who loves blue stones to chase down a good example. It has the strength of its own blue, and can, when properly cut, have great sparkle and hold its own when set with other stones.

The pink topaz at its best is an almost "ruddy" color, a bright, deep red-pink, more red than rose, and with no trace of yellow. Almost without exception, the pink topaz is a heat-treated sherry-yellow Brazilian stone. Very rarely does pink topaz occur in nature. It is a lovely stone: feminine without being insipid, and is at its most exquisite in a brilliant or step cut where, thanks to its hardness, it can dazzle marvelously. It was much admired and used by the Victorians, but it is quite rare.

Along with other great pinks—the pink diamond, sapphire, tourmaline, kunzite, morganite, and the spinel—pink topaz lends itself to diamond settings and also to other stones with a blue cast: aquamarines, some green tourmalines, and light sapphires.

There is a pale blue-green topaz, sometimes quite wrongly called an aquamarine, but its color lacks vitality, and too many other blue-green stones are a more enticing shade.

Tourmaline

XXV

*T*ourmaline: from the Singhalese *toramalli*. Hexagonal crystals, 3-, 6-, or 9-sided, striated vertically, with a hardness of 7 to 7½.
What to look for: brilliance, deep clear colors, green African stones.
Where found: Africa, Brazil, the Urals, Ceylon, Burma, Maine, California, Madagascar.

The tourmaline is beautiful in green, red, pink, amethyst, many delightful blues, and even when it is colorless. The tourmaline is what you might call the stoneman's stone. It is extremely, even fascinatingly, complex as to chemical composition, as it contains a greater variety of chemical elements than any other mineral and the chemical composition can vary from stone to stone. Tourmalines transcend all gem stones in pyroelectricity. When they are slightly warmed, one end becomes charged with positive electricity and the other end acquires a negative charge. When the stone cools, the charges are reversed. One feels, uneasily, that the tourmaline is trying to say something.

Dr. Kunz, in *The Magic of Jewels and Charms*, reports that Benjamin Franklin was, quite understandably, enchanted with the tourmalines that had been sent to him from London by Dr. Haberden, and he put them to work at once. The larger one he had set in a pivot ring so that either the positive or the negative side could be turned outward, and he noted as a curious circumstance that when he wore it the natural heat of his finger sufficed to charge the stone, causing it to attract light bodies.

They look harmless enough—charming, colorful crystals—but the two ends of the crystal are quite different. Further, some Brazilian tourmalines (called "watermelon" tourmaline) grow with a red core and a green outside, and in California green is at the core and the red outside, making one think of the way water swirls down the drain in South America in the opposite direction from its spiral north of the equator. Mineralogically speaking, the tourmaline is anything but a bore: a beautiful, complex, lawless character.

Tourmaline came originally, it seems, from Ceylon, which produced a yellowish and greenish variety. The yellow variety the Singhalese thought were yellow zircons,

154   Benjamin Franklin. Portrait by David Martin, 1767.

and the greenish variety they took to be peridot. It took years to get the tourmaline sorted out, which is why one thinks of the stone as being a comparatively recent discovery. Actually it has been in use for ages, but under various noms de plume.

You look for both color and purity in the tourmaline. Sparkle, of course, is determined by the cut of the stone, but as it is a good hard crystal the potential is there. As a fine tourmaline is highly transparent, one thing to avoid is the overlarge table, for then you can see right through it. So the table cut is not ideal for the tourmaline, and the cabochon is a waste. In fact, the tourmaline can be faceted all over, Indian style, or step-cut or brilliant-cut, any of which treatments allows the full barrage of color to blaze.

The colors are splendid, and, as the tourmaline is such a maverick, most colors come in a number of shades. The green tourmaline, in particular, runs the range of bottle green to light grass green. The rare red tourmaline, sometimes called rubelite, really is not red at all. It is one of the most exciting colors of all the precious stones, like sleek and glistening melted copper, poured over a deep, deep rose, sparkling and oddly metallic. It responds vividly both to gold and diamonds. Another unique color is the blue tourmaline that comes from Africa. It is a bright, dark, near peacock blue, and there is nothing like it in the whole nether world. Well cut and well set, this strange and mysterious stone can stand up against any of the great ones for beauty. As it has no fire, the ideal setting for it is with diamonds.

The peacock-blue stone, when heat-treated, turns a brilliant emerald green. But one wonders why this is ever done, when its own, natural color is unique, and green is anything but.

The yellow tourmaline is a friendly, sunny stone but, unhappily for it, runs into direct competition with the precious topaz, the golden beryl, the yellow sapphire, and citrine, to name a few, and on color it does not often come out the winner.

XXVI

Turquoise

*T*urquoise: from the thirteenth-century French *pierre turquois,* "Turkish stone."
Pliny called it "Callias." Crystalline aggregate with a hardness of 5 to 6.
What to look for: blue, and only blue, luster and the least porosity possible.
Where found: Iran and the Southwestern United States, chiefly.

The name "Turkish stone" is misleading. Actually, the turquoise was, and is,
mined in Persia, but it was taken over the hills to Turkey and sold there to early
French and Italian traders. The Persian word is *ferozah,* which means "victorious," and
it is too bad that it lost its true name and its symbolism. Still, perhaps turquoise is a
better name than "Arizonois" or "Sinai stone."

It is easy to see why turquoise was chosen as it was first sighted. It took man a
little while to unlock the beauty of a corundum crystal or find charm in a frosty-
looking pebble which no one had told him was a diamond, but the minute his ax, or
a natural upheaval, exposed that most glorious blue, he would have clawed it out of the
rock. It is a color that needs no explanation or education to appreciate. It is not an
acquired taste. When it is good it is a blue that defies criticism. Looking at it you think,
of course, of sky—a summer sky, and the very color that *should* back the columns of
the Parthenon, or pulse over a curving Italian hill town, or delineate the white marble
of a Persian minaret. Sometimes a southern sea is this color—but not often. It is a sky
stone, for all its lack of transparency and waxy luster. Turquoise alone of the opaque
stones lets you look into it. Other opaque stones—such as violet-blue lapis, or a fine
green malachite—display their color at arm's length. They will not, so to speak, let you
"in" as a fine sapphire will, and sometimes an amethyst, or the right shade of peridot,
and as a good turquoise always does. Turquoise is the only stone that wears the
archaic smile.

Because turquoise can look beautiful set in either gold or silver, the early peoples
used it as adornment as often as they found it. It was also one of the earliest amulets
known, and has always been associated—for heaven knows what reason—with horses,
falls from horses, runaway horses, and injuries to and from horses.

Man's knowledge and appreciation of turquoise is very old. Four turquoise-and-gold bracelets are probably the oldest pieces of man-made jewelry known. For seventy-five hundred years they have encircled the arm of the mummy of Queen Zer of Egypt.

Queen Zer's stones may have been a lucky find in some stream—for turquoise is sometimes found in the beds of rivers as nodules—but as it is not very hard, it cannot survive being battered by stone and water for very long, so it is more likely to have been mined. It is definitely known that as early as 5500 B.C. turquoise *was* being mined.

The oldest existing mines are those in the Mahara Wadi on the Sinai Peninsula. By 3200 B.C. the Egyptian kings sent expeditions there for the sole purpose of mining. It was an organized industry, with two and sometimes three thousand workers protected by a large military escort. Along with turquoise they also brought from these expeditions malachite, black manganese, and copper, the latter used for glazes and enamels that still delight the eye in museums and collections. This particular mine was worked consecutively for two thousand years—or, it was thought, until the turquoise gave out. It fell into oblivion, only to be rediscovered in 1945 by a Major McDonald.

Next oldest are the Persian mines, and from these came the finest turquoise in the world. It is not only the perfect blue—untouched by green, yellow, white, or black—but it is also a little less porous than other turquoise and takes a superb polish.

Porosity is the weakness of turquoise. In time, dirt, soap, perspiration can discolor it and give it a greenish tinge, and even the minuscule quartz particles in the air can scratch it. On the other hand, the Egyptian turquoise starts out that way, as either greenish-blue or a yellowish-green or sometimes an almost apple-green shade. So the color you see in ancient tombs, inlays, statuettes, mummy beads, and scarabs, is not due entirely to atmosphere and use. Also, as the Egyptian turquoise is slightly more porous than either the Persian or the American turquoise, it could not take quite so fine a polish.

As with the opal and pearls, one has to accept a certain mortality: in turquoise color dies. There have been many methods of trying to return the blue to a turquoise, but none of them is entirely satisfactory because none of them do this permanently. Turquoises should be cared for. Their ideal situation is as tiara or drop earrings, where they touch neither skin nor soap and water; and are free from contact with perspiration or face powder, they only have dust particles to cope with. While most stones are becoming, turquoise is extremely flattering to every skin tone, black, white, red, and yellow, and since time immemorial the members of every race have known this and made the most of it.

Another thing about turquoise: think of a round piece of pure blue turquoise, then put it on imaginary sheets of paper in every color you can think of. There is no color that is not happy at the light, fresh touch of turquoise; even near, just-off-tone blue shades look interesting. Barring the diamond, there is no other stone that meets this challenge so well.

Turquoise sets beautifully in gold, but the glossy cerulean set with diamonds might be the sky itself, blue, far-reaching, and held in check only by the host of small blazing white suns. While the deep, imperious stones can produce some rather long thoughts, the turquoise produces happy and serene ones. However, if a stone has become badly greened or is in a coarse matrix, turquoise can be quite an irritating color and seems to screech like chalk on a blackboard.

In the United States and Mexico there is a beautiful blue turquoise, less intense than the Persian example, but light blue like a clear spring sky. There is also the bluish-green and the greenish-blue shade. A good deal of it comes from the Southwestern states, New Mexico being the greatest producer, and it has been mined since—no one knows for sure.

To this day the Navajos in particular mine it, sell it, and carry a bit of it around them, either as a talisman or as a mobile work of art, especially turquoise matrix.

Turquoise matrix is turquoise so enmeshed and embedded in the mother stone that it cannot be removed—or if it were, all one would have left would be chips. It can be quite beautiful, or quite ugly. The best form of matrix turquoise is called "spider web" because its visible matrix is thin and delicate. When the matrix is thick and heavy the stone, for all its glorious color, looks crude, uncomfortable, and oddly hot and thirsty, but turquoise matrix can be a wonderful refreshment as a box or ornament. Against dark wood or on a mirrored table top or a white wood overmantel, it suddenly becomes an object of exquisite delicacy and vividness—a small sky in the parlor. The same piece set in a silver arm band looks strong but primitive and rough, and is glamorous only when worn by those who truly know how to wear it—the Navajo and the Pueblo Indians, for instance. It means something special to these people and that fact seems to come through. They wear a great deal of it, and worn this way, in bulk, matrix turquoise looks bluer and more dynamic.

The Aztecs wore it, the Incas wore it, the Egyptians wore it. The Persians not only wore it but decorated tables, thrones, and niches with it. In 1604 Boris Godunov had a thank-you present from the great Persian Shah Abbas: a throne covered with eight hundred and twenty-five good-sized turquoises, one of them enormous (which is rare), any number of small bordering turquoises, plus five hundred and fifty-two rubies and one hundred and seventy-seven whole pearls. The Empress Josephine had a glorious parure of turquoises and diamonds, and possibly the prettiest if not the most valuable diadem of the Russian crown jewels were ovals of velvety cerulean Persian turquoise scrolled about with good-sized diamonds.

Turquoise is obligingly near the surface, which is one reason it was mined so early It is rarely more than a hundred feet down, which partially accounts for its comparatively pleasant price. Mining is fairly simple. Elaborate equipment is not necessary. Almost always the turquoise is cut cabochon—not matter what its shape. Somehow the mild or deep curve—the sky curve—brings out its truest beauty.

XXVII

Zircon

Z ircon: from the French *jargon* and the Sanskrit *rehurtna*. Tetragonal system of
prismatic crystals with a hardness of 7½.
What to look for: purity, color, good cut.
Where found: Cambodia, Ceylon, Australia.

Anyone taking the trouble to study the vital statistics of the zircon must wonder
why it doesn't rank higher on the roster of the precious few. It stands next but one
to the diamond for fire. It has the hard adamantine luster, which is usually the
sole property of the diamond. It is harder than quartz and only half a step down from
topaz. It is a stone that has been in use—and respected—at least since the thirteenth
century B.C. in Egypt. It is the jacinth and the hyacinth of the epics and the Bible and
romances of the Middle Ages. There are references to it in Greek and Roman times; for
the past millennium it was in the royal inventories as a gem worthy of separate listing.

As a stone the zircon lacks nothing; all one can say against it is that is comes in
the group of orange-yellow-brown gems that appeal less to present taste. For the stone
to have been revered for so many thousands of years brings up a question: Is it possible that today we have lost our sensitivity to color? Must everything be in neon
versions of red or green or blue? It looks rather like it.

The natural zircons, when they are well cut, speak in clear, bright voices. Care-
lessly, one might call them "brown"; but they are about as brown as a harvest moon.
They blaze with light and warmth and, when they are well cut, fire off the spectrum
colors. Some of them look like an orange seen through amber; some, with husky voices,
are darker than sherry. Sometimes their fire darts from a light mahogany shade, and
sometimes we see a bright and dazzling apricot-gold. In their natural state they are
for the expert who knows what a noble stone the zircon is, or for the stone sophisti-
cate, or for the very subtle.

About 1921 there suddenly appeared in the markets of the world a blue zircon.
A clear animated Alice blue, with startling fire and brilliance. Gemmologists and mineralogists look at each other in blank astonishment. An intense blue zircon? How?

From where? Finally the truth was unearthed: the beautiful blue zircon was quite simply that old stand-by the jacinth (the yellow-brown zircon) heat-treated. For centuries the Siamese had been quietly changing the color of the stones they brought down from Cambodia, baking them in the most primitive charcoal furnaces, often inside a loaf of bread, and in complete secrecy. What is more, by varying temperature and atmosphere, they could at will create pale-yellow zircons and colorless ones. The colorless ones, with all their fire and brilliance, were often erroneously sold for diamonds in the days before scientific testing—as often as not sold by early jewelers in perfect good faith.

The zircon, under one or another of its aliases, has a long history. The Sanskrit name for hyacinth (the red-gold stone) unveils the fact that it was a stone dedicated to the mysterious dragon who caused the periodic eclipse of the sun and the moon. The stone represented in that case a huge, malefic power and received the most apprehensive deference.

For some time there was a question as to whether or not it was the jacinth (the yellow-brown stone) or amber that was allotted as the seventh stone in the High Priest's Breastplate, but the Greek naturalist Theophrastus, in the fourth century B.C., laid special stress on the coldness of the substance, and as that is a characteristic of the zircon and all crystalline stones, it settled firmly into its setting. If you accept that, then it was also the eleventh of the Foundation Stones of the New Jerusalem.

The name "hyacinth" brings up a puzzle of its own. The stone was named for that beautiful youth beloved of Apollo, who was slain by Zephyr out of jealousy and from whose blood sprang the hyacinth flower, probably the wild hyacinth of Greece, which is blue. Because reddish-yellow is hardly a color associated with the hyacinth, is it possible that a heat-treated zircon could have been known then? As in the tale of how roast pork was first invented (the peasant's hut burned down with the pig inside), could a brown zircon have fallen into a fire and come up blue? Or could those secretive Siamese have been nursing their secret even then? Or did it represent his blood?

It must be said of the zircon that, like any beauty, it has one or two potential weaknesses. In time a heat-treated stone can begin to lose its luster, fade, and the stone begin to return to its true color. It need not, but it can. Slowly the golden shade reasserts itself, so it is wise to make sure a zircon is entirely free of any yellow tones when you buy it. Any hint of yellow or gold or green can mean that it is already on its way home—which might account for the fact that there is no ancient blue zircon. Another weakness: the girdle of a zircon *can* chip or nick, but so can many stones. So the moral of that is: protect your stone.

XXVIII

Lyric Stones

There are the epic stones: the great ones, the ancient, the renowned, and they are also the great beauties. But then in the world of crystals, as in our own, there is something else that must never be overlooked—charm. This attribute belongs to a host of happy, undemanding crystals; stones that might be said to be easy and relaxed, that do not take themselves too seriously, that do not need a ball to go to, stones, in fact, that are light, lovely, inexpensive, and often have the kudos of scarcity as well.

Often these lyrical stones are too soft to win the complete approval of the responsible jeweler (who, one sometimes feels, like the family lawyer, really has one's great-grandchild in mind), but chiefly they are unknown and unsung. Because they cannot—and should not, of course—command the prices of the epic stones, they are often not considered worth the expense of mining. The result of this is that they are often as scarce as many of the great stones.

When they are found, good and well-cut examples are to be treasured. A number of them should be protectively set—not buried in a setting, but just protected at the edges, much as one might wrap a scarf around the neck of a child with the sniffles. Among a handful of these delightful crystals are the following:

Spodumene, a species of pyroxene which, along with precious jade, includes two particular beauties: kunzite, clear as a crystal bell, in lilac pink to nearly lilac blue, a stone which loves diamonds and shows it; and hiddenite, a rare (and getting rarer) crystal found, ideally, in a fine emerald green, and upward in the scale to a greenish absinthe yellow. Kunzite is no problem to find, but hiddenite is very scarce.

Benitoite was discovered only in 1907, which, when we consider how long any crystal has been inexistence, is astonishing. When benitoite was first found in San Benito County, California (its only source), it was thought to be sapphire, as the color is what one might call corundum blue and corundum violet. It has a color dispersion close to the diamond, a good glassy luster, and a hardness of $6\frac{1}{2}$, a far cry from sapphire's 8, but as hard as many great gems. It is a lovely stone, the blue shade in particular, but unfortunately it seems to form only in small crystals and is too rare.

Apatite is extremely attractive and comes in a large palette: yellow, green, pink, blue, purple, and violet. It is such a charming crystal that one hesitates to remember

162

that, like most phosphates, it is made of the droppings and remains of prehistoric animals. It has a glassy luster or sometimes the greasy luster of the opal, and its hardness is 5, which means it can be scratched with a knife blade and needs loving care.

Diopside is sometimes found in clear, limpid crystals, usually in a fine bottle green, but sometimes an element of chromium has been introduced and the green moves up to a far brighter shade. There is also a warm shade of blue, which comes only from Piedmont, Italy. Its hardness is 6—quite respectable—and its luster glassy. Recently many cat's-eye and star diopsides have been exported from India.

Dioptase is a dazzling crystal which has the impertinence closely to resemble the emerald, and even crystallizes in the same hexagonal system. Its hardness, however, is only 5, and it is rarely cut. It is scarce and in constant demand, and crystals should be seized on sight.

Sphene reads like a description of what a great stone should be: it has more fire than the diamond and is dichromatic besides, and on top of that it has an adamantine luster. It comes in fine shades of a rather strong yellow and lightish, brightish green. Well cut (and anything else would be criminal with all that fire and brilliance), it fairly leaps out its setting. Its hardness is sometimes 5 and sometimes 5½, which admittedly is hard only compared with coral.

Euclase is beautiful but rare. Collectors pursue it, for its uncut crystals are elegant and prismatic, with lovely smooth faces, and in gentle sea green and sea blue, as intense as a fine aquamarine, with the same clear, watery feeling. It is a good hard 7½ but has one most unfortunate failing: a too easy cleavage (it separates where *it* chooses) so the untouched crystal is better on a mantel or in a well-lit cabinet than on a finger.

Phenakite comes from the Greek word meaning "cheat," because it so closely resembles quartz. Perhaps the shoe should be on the other foot, for phenakite is even harder than quartz, varying from 7½ to 8. It is found both in a pale yellow and a soft, light rose red, neither of which, of course, can compete with the splendid crimson-pink of a good spinel or the liveliness of a fine citrine. Still, it has the same glassy luster as quartz and emerald, and is a pretty rather than a grand stone.

Acknowledgments

With profound thanks to all those—from Theophrastus to Tiffany's—who were good enough to offer me their assistance on this very complex subject. I am in debt to so many. I name a very few: Mr. William T. Lusk, Mr. Harry Winston, Mr. Ralph Esmerian, Mr. Oscar Heyman, Mr. Milton Schepps. My thanks, too, to extraordinarily patient curators and librarians, and the New York Public Library; to Lord Twining for his monumental work, *The Crown Jewels of Europe*, on which I leaned for the genealogy of certain historic stones. Above all, thanks to Mr. Robert Crowningshield of the New York Gemological Institute, who did me the great kindness of vetting the whole book, to David Plowden, who worked so painstakingly on the special and difficult color photographs I wanted, and to Elizabeth Otis for her humor and patience with first drafts.

My thanks, too, to those gentlemen of the past who could use pen or stylus and who loved or noticed crystals: to Pliny for his precise and critical works, to Anselmo de Boot for being so airily positive about the sex and temperature of stones, to Baron Tavernier for his delightful and exact reminiscences; and for the scholarship of Dr. George F. Kunz, and the spacious knowledge of Edward Streeter, Robert Shipley, Robert Webster, G. F. Herbert Smith, Chester Baker Slawson, and Edward Henry Kraus.

The author and publishers would also like to thank the following for their kind permission to reproduce the illustrations in this book: (Frontispiece) A.C.L., Brussels. (Page 6) The Museum of Fine Arts, Boston. (13) The New York Public Library. (15) 200-inch photograph; Mount Wilson and Palomar Observatories, California. (16) Title page of the edition of Marbodus on Precious Stones, Cologne, 1539. (17) "L'Homme Anatomique" by Pol de Limbourg; 15th century; from the *Très Riches Heures* of the Duc de Berry; photo: Giraudon, Paris. (19) From *A Guide to the Collection of Gemstones in the Geological Museum* by Dr. W. F. P. McLintock, 3rd ed.; revised by Dr. P. A. Sabine; Her Majesty's Stationery Office, London, 1951. (21, 22) Robert Crowningshield. (24) From *Gemstones* by G. F. Herbert Smith; rev.

164

ed. by F. C. Phillips; Methuen & Co., Ltd., London, 1962. (29) Photo: Giraudon, Paris. (34) *Vogue*, New York. (37) Germanisches Nationalmuseum, Nürnberg. (38) Copy of the jewel; watercolor on parchment, 15th century; Historiches Museum, Basel. (39) Radio Times Hulton Picture Library, London. (41) The Louvre. (45, left) Phoenician bust found at Elche, Spain; the Louvre. (45, right) Terracotta sarcophagus cover; 2nd century B.C.; British Museum. (46) From *The History of Fashion in France* by M. Augustin Challamel; (English translation) London, 1882. (47) Museo Poldi Pezzoli, Milan. (48, 49) From *Modes et Costumes Historiques*, Pauquet Frères, Paris. (51) Dr. Helmut Gernsheim. (81) Oscar Heyman and Bros., Inc.; photo: Nicolas Ducrot. (82) New York Public Library Picture Collection. (87) European Picture Service. (91) Keystone Press Agency, Inc. (97, right) University Museum, Philadelphia. (97, left) Trésor de l'Archevêche de Reims; photo: Mgr. Berton, Paroisse Notre-Dame, Reims. (101) Freelance Photographers' Guild, Inc. (104) Boston Public Library. (109) Bibliothèque Nationale, Paris. (110, left) *Modes et Costumes Historiques*, Pauquet Frères. (110, upper right) Harry Winston, Inc., New York. (110-111, center) Academia San Fernando, Madrid; photo: Foto Mas, Barcelona. (111, upper left) The Louvre. (111, upper right) Taft Museum, Cincinnati. (113) Radio Times Hulton Picture Library. (114) The Metropolitan Museum of Art; Gift of J. Pierpoint Morgan, 1917. (119) M. H. de Young Memorial Museum, San Francisco. (120) Design by Jean Schlumberger, Tiffany & Co. (125) From the *Hortus Sanitatis* of Johannis de Cuba, Strassburg, 1483. (127, 132, 133) Bibliothèque Nationale. (135) Unknown artist; National Portrait Gallery; photo: Keystone Press Agency, Inc. (137) St. James's Palace, London; photo: A. C. Cooper, Ltd.; copyright reserved. (139) Radio Times Hulton Picture Library; photo: Roger Fenton, 1854. (140) Design by Jean Schlumberger, Tiffany & Co. (148) The Queen's Collection, Buckingham Palace; photo: The Art Engravers, Ltd. (151) The Smithsonian Institution, Freer Gallery of Art, Washington, D.C. (155) White House Historical Association, Washington.

Credit for the gems appearing in the color plates is due to:
1. Traders in Treasurers; photo: Horst. 2. Oscar Heyman and Bros., Inc.; photo: Nicolas Ducrot. 3. R. Esmerian, Inc. 4. Metropolitan Museum of Art. 5. Tiffany & Co. 6. R. Esmerian, Inc. 7. B. Hoffman. 8. Neiman Marcus. 9. Harry Winston, Inc. 10. Harry Winston, Inc.; *Life*; photo: Gehr. 11, 12. Tiffany & Co. 13. The Queen's Collection, England. 14. Tiffany & Co. 15. Van Cleef and Arpels, Inc. 16. Milton Schepps. 17. Imperial Pearl Syndicate, Inc. 18. Tiffany & Co. 19. Cartier, Inc. 20. New York Gemological Institute. 21. William V. Schmidt, Inc. 22. Milton Schepps. 23. William V. Schmidt, Inc. 24. Neiman Marcus. 25. Cartier, Inc. 26. Milton Schepps. 27. Van Cleef & Arpels, Inc. 28. R. Esmerian, Inc.

All color plates, unless otherwise indicated, were taken for this book by David Plowden.

Index

(Figures in italics refer to illustrations)